Other Books by

MARY DILLINGHAM FREAR

THE COCOA PALM AND OTHER
SONGS FOR CHILDREN
[WORDS AND MUSIC]

MY ISLANDS
[VERSE]

HAWAIIAN DAYS AND HOLIDAYS AND
DAYS OF LONG AGO
[VERSE]

OVER TWO SEAS
THE LOG OF A SPINSTER

FLAME TREE (Ponciana regia)

OUR FAMILIAR
ISLAND TREES

❧

MARY DILLINGHAM FREAR

Sponsored by
THE OUTDOOR CIRCLE OF HONOLULU

WITH ILLUSTRATIONS

ARTI et VERITATI

BOSTON
RICHARD G. BADGER
THE GORHAM PRESS

PRINTED IN THE UNITED STATES OF AMERICA

TO THE MEMORY OF
CHERILLA L. LOWREY
WHO IS STILL AN INSPIRATION
TO OUR OUTDOOR CIRCLE

To me the meanest flower that blows can give
Thoughts that do often lie too deep for tears.

Wordsworth.

FOREWORD

In preparing this little book the attempt has been made to comply with a request from the Outdoor Circle to furnish for the use of both resident and stranger a simple guide to the familiar trees, shrubs and vines about us. Description inevitably if not necessarily means that one picture the thing as he sees it. The reader is free to differ in interpretation and personal reaction.

To deal with the familiar is to woo one's soul into forbidden paths of the unfamiliar, the undreamed-of darks and mysteries of the great company of indigenous plants hidden away in remote and sometimes inaccessible forests. Just to mention the fact that these small islands hold among their indigenous plants a larger proportion of endemics than does any other spot on the globe, is to lift a curtain on deep questions. But that is not for us.

Strange as it may seem, almost all the plant growth seen in the city and its environs is imported. Of the more than two hundred plants mentioned here less than twenty (including several varieties of native palm) are indigenous.

But in the vegetable kingdom as in the human world there are those that by affinity with their surroundings become *kamaaina*, "of the land." In both realms a *malahini* (stranger) in name may be *kamaaina* at heart.

Among our human *kamaainas* who has an eye keen enough to mark the subtle changes of tropical seasons when a summer sun shines in a winter sky, a winter rain drops through a summer night, leaves fall in the spring, birds mate in the fall, winter vines bloom on till May and summer trees begin to flower in March?

Generally speaking, as if to make each season the choicest in Hawaii nature brings the vines to bloom during the months of "winter" and the trees in "summer" but there is a merry overstepping of bounds in her tropic household, an excess of vitality that anticipates the beginnings and never makes an end of bloomtime. One or another delights to tell of a pear or a mango tree in his garden that bears a little fruit each month in the year. However the calendar expects the blare of little orange-colored trumpets on the *bignonia venusta* to usher in the new year and to start the floral procession. After the pageant of flowering trees is over the coming of winter finds Honolulu wrapped not in the ermine of snow but nevertheless in the purple of everblooming bougainvillea.

ACKNOWLEDGMENTS

For botanical terminology and for the few scientific statements of these pages I am indebted to the not now easily accessible books of J. F. Rock, "The Indigenous Trees of the Hawaiian Islands" and "The Ornamental Trees of Hawaii," Dr. William Hillebrand's "Flora of the Hawaiian Islands," W. A. Bryan's "Natural History of Hawaii," G. P. Wilder's "Fruits of the Hawaiian Islands," C. M. Woodrow's "Gardening in the Tropics" and H. F. Macmillan's "Tropical Gardening and Planting"; also to Mr. Charles Judd, Mr. David Haughs, Professor Herbert F. Bergman, Mr. W. T. Pope, Dr. Harold Lyon, and Mr. Edward Caum who have patiently answered questions.

Sincere thanks are due and are here expressed for the loan by the Bernice Pauahi Bishop Museum of negatives of photographs by Dr. Brigham, Charles Furneaux and Alonzo Gartley—tree lovers deceased. Acknowledgment is made of photographs from the Williams Studio and the Shimizu Photo Studio. Especial mention must be made of the cooperation of Ray J. Baker, photographer, the gift of pictures and other kindly services.

Mahalo

M. D. F.

CONTENTS

xii

ILLUSTRATIONS

xiii

OUR FAMILIAR ISLAND TREES

THE ACANTHUS FAMILY

Blue Allamanda

Thunbergia grandiflora

Not forgetting the thrill it was to gather true Acanthus leaves in Sicily near the ancient Greek theatre where under summer skies the drama of Euripides is reproduced today, it is pleasant to find that classic family represented in Honolulu by no less beautiful a vine than the *Thunbergia grandiflora,* a native of India. This is one of our most lusty growths; rapidity, size and virility of stem vying for preëminence. The clusters of blue-lilac flowers, with the entire corolla scalloped at edge but depressed on one side as in the Bignonia family, make an exquisite contrast in color to the large bottle-green, pointed leaves. It is very decorative, but is one of the most difficult flowers to keep from wilting when cut. "Try, try again!"

Thunbergia affinis

This is a small-leaved shrub much grown as a dainty hedge. Its flowers resemble those of the *Thunbergia grandiflora* in shape but are much smaller and the petals, ending with the white tube, are deep purple in color. It, also, is a native of India.

A white variety is a new importation.

PHILIPPINE VIOLET

Barleria strigosa

Another hedge plant, this has lavender flowers. It
is grown at the edge of a lawn at the University of
Hawaii, and is becoming a garden favorite.

ARALIA FAMILY

ARALIA

Brassaia actinophylla

Called usually by the euphonious name of its family
which is so slightly represented in Hawaii, this tree,
a most ornamental house plant if kept for a few years
in tubs, grows to a height of forty feet yet retains
slender and graceful proportions as branches from
near the ground spring daughter-like beside it. Its
handsome leathery leaflets are arranged like ten-
fingered hands on long delicate stalks and its red
flowers, followed by purple-black fruits, cling closely
to long stems flung forth in the manner of certain
colorful, gelatinous "sea serpents" seen in the shoals
of Pearl Harbor.

PANAX

Nothopanax guilfoylei

Dark green leaves with white ruffled edges, borne
thickly upon shrubs rapidly attaining a shapely height,
make the Panax a favorite hedge plant. It does not
flower in Honolulu but is easily propagated from short,

woody cuttings set at a slant in a well-watered ditch. Some care has to be used lest the rapid upper growth of the hedge leave the woody base meagrely clothed with leaves. Fresh plants may be set out to remedy this or the bark may be scarred to start adventitious buds.

BAMBOO FAMILY

Common Bamboo —— Ohe

Bambusa vulgaris

Several species of Bamboo are to be found in the islands. The earliest and commonest, *Bambusa vulgaris,* sometimes found wild in the woods, was, according to Dr. Hillebrand, probably brought here from China in the early part of the nineteenth century. Its use by the Hawaiian is slight compared with its use by peoples elsewhere but it gives him the usual fishing pole and sometimes parts of canoe outriggers. In olden times long single joints of bamboo were made into nose-flutes from which issued plaintively-breathed tones like bird notes used as lovers' calls.

The delicate Bamboo of Japan is cultivated for decorative purposes and occasionally, as on the Round Top drive, one sees the Bamboo with large bright yellow stems. In a pocket of the Manoa woods, the Common Bamboo makes a forest and, when wandering through the dusk of lofty green poles that give a constantly clicking sound from their close contact, one may receive new sensations of nature's pleasuring.

3

BANANA FAMILY

Banana —— Maia

Musa (in varieties)

Speaking of antiquity, hats off to the Banana!

Very likely pre-Columbian in reaching the Americas, the Banana is hundreds of thousands of years old, is indigenous not only in Hawaii but in other tropical countries, and perhaps antedates man on the globe. Always his close friend, giving him food and shelter, it has been dependent upon man for cultivation and distribution through the world. The Banana was originally seed-bearing and offered its root rather than its fruit as food. Its variations, development and improvement are remarkable. The wild forms of today are supposed to be escapes from cultivation.

A child passing by a large Banana plantation, where the old stalks, having borne each its one bunch of fruit were being cut down to make room for the lusty suckers that would more than take their places, asked "Is life like a Banana plantation?" The young philosopher's question held its answer. The life-work of the Banana is done in a twelvemonth when the huge purple-red flower-bud pushes its way through the crowning leaves of the tree and, because of its heavy burden, begins curving toward the ground. It unfolds one by one the leathery bracts that shield the creamy tubular flowers. After the marriage of the two kinds of flower, the fertilized tubes develop into the rich, nourishing fruit known in so many colors of skin and flesh, so many shapes, sizes and flavors, there being forty-two varieties of Banana known in Hawaii. The long stem

4

CHINESE BANANA TREE

with its last and useless flowers often hangs far below the bunch and is cut off for conservation of the fructified part. The tree, before winds have tattered its magnificent, long, graceful leaves with their unspeakably immaculate surface, is a feast to the eye.

Naturally so rapid a growth feeds prodigiously on the soil and suckers are transplanted for propagation to pastures new to keep up the value of the product.

The Chinese or Cavendish Banana is grown extensively for export, its short, stocky stem being wind-resistant and its strength going into the size of the bunch. The bunch is picked when still green, though matured, wrapped in its own leaves, and, since like the Coconut and Pineapple it is self-protected from the ravages of the fruit-fly, is loaded upon steamers for distant markets. A few of the native varieties and certain others (some of which are used only when cooked) are preferred above the Chinese Banana by Honolulu residents. Of these one occasionally finds in market the large Red Banana, familiar elsewhere, the Ice-Cream Banana with an exceedingly delicate pulp inclosed in a skin suggesting turquoise blue velvet; and commonly, a large or a small snub-nosed Banana with heavy dark yellow skin, used only for cooking, but when baked and eaten with butter a delectable dish; the small pale yellow, curved fruit known from its taste as the Apple Banana; the larger straighter Brazilian Banana, delicious and rich in flavor and borne on a tall stately tree; the *Ihulena,* a coveted indigenous variety, its thin pale yellow, black-spotted skin peeling back to show a pulp of creamy salmon color. The Lady Finger variety, descriptively named, is too rare for market but should be a favorite in the garden of an epicure.

Perhaps a use of the Banana yet to be developed is an indelible ink which resides in the sap against the stains of which from skin, stem, broken leaf or trunk the unwary must be warned.

TRAVELLER'S PALM

Ravenala madagascariensis

Once again a nickname is a misnomer, for this strikingly handsome member of the Banana family is not a Palm and the tales we loved when we were children, of travellers coming upon the vessels of water held high by this tree for human need, are as idle talk to the mind of the scientist. Its true name tells its birthplace but it has for fifty years or more been at home in Hawaii. Not so graceful as some of its Banana cousins, it is far more sophisticated. About two dozen leaves, each twelve or more feet long, are arranged in a fan-like pattern, one fan above another, calling for some titan hand like that of Boreas to wield them. And how he responds, shredding these leaves as he does those of the Banana!

Seed may be used for propagation but suckers are easily obtainable.

LOBSTER CLAW

Heliconia brasilensis

The claws of an eastern lobster perched on the edge of a boiling pot are not redder than the strange bracts of this *Heliconia*. Its leaf suggests that of cousin Banana and its claw-like vessels somewhat pattern after the water holders of the Traveller's Palm.

7

BIRD OF PARADISE

Strelitzia reginae

In this land of ever blooming beauty it may be a shock to learn of one flower that is kept under lock and key. It is the Bird of Paradise that is indeed so

BIRD OF PARADISE

rare a bird as literally to be çaged—lest it offer too great a temptation to change ownership! Its strange floral plumage is a combination of orange and electric blue and the delicate "wings" nestled against the long leaves seem poised for flight.

8

BEAN FAMILY

ALGAROBA —— Kiawe

Prosopis julifera

As one looks down from Punchbowl, the crater-hill back of the business section of Honolulu, the city is embedded, like a jewel in thick cotton, in the delicate moss-like foliage of the ubiquitous Algaroba. It is the Mesquite of South America, but its size and value are greater in this favoring climate than in its native land. It, or its nearest kin, claims to have been the Carob tree on the fruit whereof the Prodigal Son would fain have stayed his hunger. The writer has recognized it on the banks of the Nile.

For its relation to the vegetation of Honolulu and its environs, in history, results and symbolism, it may be called a pocket-edition-missionary. The pioneer seed was planted by Father Bachelot one hundred years ago and in its shade was built the Cathedral of Our Lady of Peace. Alas, the tree in its grandeur of venerable years was slain to make way for a Club House. Its huge trunk, propped against a wall in the Mission garden, continued to send forth sporadic twigs a decade later.

The dissemination of the tree is interesting. School children were taught to carry seed pods in their pockets and to scatter them as they walked across the arid plains between town and Punahou. Pods were also fed to pasturing horses and in a few years those miles parched and cracked by the unmitigated rays of the sun, growing only Kikania (*Datura stramonium*) and

9

ALGAROBA TREES AND COCONUT PALMS

other weeds and the thorny shrub Kalu (*Acacia farnesiana*) bore a thicket of Algarobas many of which grew to magnificent height and girth in the following fifty years. Much were its praises sung—its adaptation to poor soil, its growth without cultivation, its lightness of shade allowing grass beneath it, its swiftness of growth, its offering of hard wood for fires, even burning green, the excellence of the fodder from the fruit, the honey from its flowers. But one of its characteristics has proved to be not only its salvation but its destruction. The Algaroba has no tap root but in too shallow soil spreads a mass of small roots like a many fingered hand with open palm grasping for sustenance almost regardless of support. Its trusting branches spread with the breadth and lightsomeness of an Elm but when winter comes, if heavy rains precede stormy gales, trees of forty or fifty years' growth are overturned as easily as a chess board is dismantled by a kitten, and the giants lie with their roots of false hope standing twenty feet in the air. Since the city has thus lost hundreds of her oldest trees, the Inga, Monkey-pod and others are replacing the former favorite. Nothing really takes the place, however, of this large and graceful shade tree. One looks always up through its interlacing boughs of delicate foliage to the blue and white sky in its embrasure or to the stars entangled in its network of perennial leaves, for

> The new leaves come, the old leaves fall
> Nor naked stands the bough
> As growth indeed the soul perceives
> Only the soul knows how.

Yellow Mimosa —— Kalu

Acacia farnesiana

Is Kalu one of our prophets without honor? The sturdy, thorny wayside shrub seen on the Punchbowl drive or on the way to the Naval Station, with twice pinnate leaves and little balls of intensely fragrant petal-less flowers, suggesting in color and texture a tuft from the rare yellow feather leis of chieftains, has been considered a pest and ruthlessly swept away to make room for the green cane fields that cover the slopes from Moanalua Hill to the Waianae Range. Yet this shrub bears a small dark pod filled with seeds furnishing a valuable medicine for horses, and formerly exported to Germany for that use, while its flower, found in France, is there used as a basis for perfumes.

Koa

Acacia koa

This is the true name for the exploited "Hawaiian Mahogany" which needs no false botanical claim when its own beauty and value as a cabinet wood are known. The Koa, like the Kukui, is indigenous and although large inroads have been made upon it, unlike the sandalwood which was almost exterminated in the early days of trade with China, it is still one of the chief forest trees of Hawaii. A rapid grower, it attains a height of from fifty to sixty feet and, in the forests on "the big island," a huge girth. It is sadly noticeable that on Oahu, after attaining twenty years of age, the Koa is susceptible to insect destruction.

The timber of the Koa has a grain sometimes fine and curly, sometimes large and dark, in marking. It is capable of high polish. Unfortunately much of the Koa furniture displayed in the local shops is made from unseasoned wood and degraded by a light and shiny finish. Its natural color varies from that of imprisoned sunlight to the deep tones of old San Domingan Mahogany.

KOA TREE

The ancient Hawaiian never used Koa for his food dishes (although the contrary is often stated and many modern machine-made calabashes made of it are for sale in curio shops) as it imparts a disagreeable flavor. Nor did he use it for furniture, as he had none, nor for houses, since these were made of grass. But the Koa furnished his magnificent canoes, laboriously hollowed with crude stone adzes from mighty trunks and smoothed and polished by hand, fit to withstand for

13

many a year shock of wave, buffet of storm, and strain of hazardous landings. A few modern canoes made of Koa are much prized by their American owners and may be seen on the beach at Waikiki.

The blossom of the Koa, a little yellow ball of minute flowers that grow pale after the visits of the bees, resembles that of the Wattle, Mimosa and other familiar Acacias. The pod-borne seed is small and

KOA TREE SHOWING CRESCENT SHAPED LEAVES

brown and, when not attacked by insects, takes root where the soil is disturbed. The leaf is extraordinary. Early in the life of the tree the midrib of the compound leaf characteristic of the family becomes metamorphosed into a flat scimitar or crescent-shaped blade entirely displacing the true leaf. Occasionally from the tip of this false leaf, like a whip lash, the true leaf appears, as if to make reassertion of its origin.

14

Unlike the Kukui, the Koa is difficult to transplant. Seeds should be germinated in baskets made of leaves that will dissolve in the earth on planting without disturbing the roots. The tree rarely thrives below an altitude of one thousand feet, although it will live as high as four thousand feet. It is being much used in the reforestation of bare slopes.

To the old resident the Koa is invested with the spirit of the Islands.

Mimosa —— Koa Haole

Leucaena glauca

The first part of the Tantalus Drive climbs the slopes of Round Top (Ualakaa) through a thicket of Mimosa or Koa Haole (the Hawaiian name signifying foreign or white man's Koa). An exceedingly rapid grower, threatening always to become ubiquitous yet readily cut, as seen on this drive, it is a graceful, thornless shrub. Its leaves, twice pinnate, close at night. Its flowers, cream-colored balls about an inch in diameter, made up of stamens and pistils without petals, are, to the eyes of little girls, doll powder-puffs.

The seed pod a brown paper-like texture with pongee-colored lining is about five inches long and contains seeds very like apple seeds. These when softened in boiling water are sewed into hat bands and other useful or useless articles for sale.

Wattles

Black (*Acacia decurrens*)
Silver (*Acacia dealbata*)

In the reforestation of Tantalus Heights, begun by the Forestry Department some forty years ago, other

Acacias, kin to the native Koa were appropriately introduced. Denizens of Australia and New Zealand, where their fragrant yellow blossoms are beloved and given national significance, the Wattles have well adapted themselves to this country. As suggested by their names, the Black Wattle has a black bark and the Silver is almost blue in its light coloring throughout. The leaf is most lacey, being more finely subdivided and minute in leaflets than other Acacias here. The dense shade of the forest is not conducive to blooming and these trees should be given opportunity to display their beauty in sunny gardens.

Inga —— Opiuma

Pithecolobium dulce

The Inga, or Opiuma as the Hawaiians call it, holds the botanical name recently taken by the scientists from the Monkey-pod. It is a native of Central America and Mexico, where it has a commercial value not known here, and was brought to Hawaii about sixty years ago. Deeper rooted than the Algaroba, its enduring qualities are appealing more than formerly to lovers of trees that are at once large and umbrageous and lightsome in character of foliage. Old specimens stand on Richards St. and Beretania Street in town, showing the majestic and yet delicate attributes of the tree, and still better specimens, *mauka— waikiki* corner of Beretania and Makiki Streets. The trunk often absorbs branches which start at the ground. It wears a rough bark of greyish color and together with the graceful but thorny branches reaches a height of sixty feet. The Inga has an artistic waywardness of growth and the two-pinnate small leaves on wiry

16

branchlets suggest the charm of a gipsy's tangled tresses. The fruit resulting from the small white tufted flowers is a curly pod, shaded from green to rose color and holding in separate knobs shiny black seeds which may be strung into necklaces. These seeds are imbedded in a dry, sweet, white pulp which "when we were very young" pleased us as well as the Mynah birds.

MONKEY-POD ——— Ohai

Samanea saman

The Monkey-pod, for majesty of bearing, giant reach of trunk and limb, and grandeur of symmetrical structure, might be called the tropic Oak. Yet to cite resemblance is but to court difference. The Oak, like all proper trees of the temperate zone, curves upward to the sun, while the Monkey-pod usually sweeps downward in all-embracing shade. Like the Oak, it has a hard wood suitable for cabinet work and, in its golden brown coloring somewhat resembling the native Koa, wears a marking of huge dark rings. Unlike the Oak, the Monkey-pod is a rapid grower, starting lustily from its seed which is imbedded in a pod full of caramel-like nourishment.

In tropical America and the West Indies where it is native, the Monkey-pod is known as the Rain Tree. The Hawaiians call it by the name of an unfamiliar indigenous tree, Ohai, and have celebrated it in song. The name Monkey-pod is a literal translation of its Greek former name, *Pithecolobium saman,* but since the scientists have changed its botanical name perhaps its common name should follow suit. However, nicknames, though often unreasonable, stick. Among the earlier imported trees, some fine examples like those on Nuuanu Street opposite Bates Street are to be seen. The fine specimen in the grounds of Central Union Church on Punahou Street is about fifty years old. Impressive specimens are in the Moanalua gardens, on Makiki Street as it merges into Round Top Road, and over the Pali at Waikane.

This deep-hearted tree seems responsive to nature's rhythm of day and season. Night-fall finds its large

MONKEY-POD TREE

compound leaves drowsily folding their soft leaflets together like the hands of children at prayer, while morning beholds them flung wide in greeting. All the year enjoys the shade of the tree. Some time between March and May comes its only season of fall and torpidity. The ground is then strewn with dusty leaves and sticky black pods, unpleasantly suggestive of centipedes in appearance and disagreeable under foot. The wise gardener, however, appreciates this litter as excellent fertilizer. The tree stands naked and at rest for not more than a fortnight; then a simultaneous burst of thick, velvety, pale green leaves and dainty, pink, fragrant, staminate blossoms proclaim the annual resurrection.

White Monkey-pod or Siris Tree
Albizzia lebbek

This co-called Monkey-pod is not a favorite like the *saman,* nor does it deserve to be planted, as it often is in India, as an avenue tree. Although its flower is like that of the Monkey-pod, only green and pale yellow instead of pink and white, and much more fragrant, the tree is less noble in leaf and structure and is too long bare of foliage, weirdly rattling its seeds in their paper-like yellow pods. In the West Indies it is called Woman's Tongue!

St. Thomas Tree
Bauhinia monandra

This tree is small enough to spurn being called a shrub. It is an old resident, a native of tropical America, and now comes into a new evaluation, for, while still planted singly, it appears planted in rows and also in avenues, as in the cemetery *ewa* side Nuuanu Avenue. Its branches, spread widely for its height, give pleasant shade for its leaves are large in proportion to its size, being four or five inches long and also across. The leaves seem to have started to be heart-shaped, but, split half way down, have two lung-like lobes. These close together at nightfall like folded palms. The flower clusters hold few flowers each, but make up for number in variation of color. The general impression is bluish-pink, but some of the petals have speckles of white and streaks of yellow and deep rose. The single stamen gives the botanical name. The seed-pods, about eight inches long are brown, flat and decorative, but if they are gathered during the winter the strength of the tree is conserved for the spring flowers.

OTHER BAUHINIAS

Other Bauhinias recently introduced are the white (*alba*) and the mauve (*purpurea*). These, even more than the St. Thomas, are so suggestive of orchids as often to be called the Orchid Trees.

Tamarind

Tamarindus indica

"The wealth of Ormus or of Ind" seems wrapped in the name of this tree, Arabian for Indian date. Descriptions of travellers returning from Java where they delighted in the Tamarinds overarching the streets, make the Islander feel our loss in not following the lead of early settlers and continuing to plant the Tamarind.

In grounds *mauka* of the cemetery on the *ewa* side Nuuanu Avenue, stands a specimen known to be more than eighty years old. Other notable specimens are two adjoining the Y.W.C.A. building on the Alakea Street side and one in front of the Church of Christ Scientist on Punahou Street.

While the dense foliage, a dark blue-green, is Acacia-like and finely compounded, the tree in its height (sometimes eighty feet) and its noble contour of graceful branches upspringing from the sturdy trunk (sometimes twenty-five feet in girth) with handsomely ridged bark, suggests more than any other of our sub-tropical trees, not excepting the Algaroba, the Elm of New England.

The flower, in pretty clusters shaded from rose to yellow is too small to attract attention. It is succeeded by a pod shaped like a string bean, its far cousin, from three to six inches long and about an inch wide. The thick skin of the pod in ripening changes to a thin, light brown shell. Within the shell lie the shiny brown seeds, imbedded in an acid pulp, the consistency of jam, which makes a delicious conserve or, dissolved in water, a refreshing drink. Its medicinal value, known to the ancients and transmitted through the Arabians to Europe during the middle ages, still holds its place in its native India.

The wood, hard, heavy and of a light yellow color streaked with grey and dark at the center of the tree, takes a high polish and suggests old ivory or Sienese marble.

The acidity of the tree permeates the leaves which in falling probably affect the soil, since it seems diffi-cult to grow grass in the shade of the Tamarind. If this circumstance can not be overcome, though, probably, it can, a bed of white sand under the tree makes a pleasant base.

The Tamarind may be propagated from seed or from cuttings and cultivation of this long-lived and magnificent tree should be encouraged.

FLAME TREE

Poinciana regia (renamed *Delonix regia*)

Native in Madagascar and elsewhere, perhaps no tree in all the tropics is more eagerly sought by the traveller as a revelation of vegetative splendor than the *Poinciana regia*. "You have seen the scarlet trees!" exclaims Stevenson in his "Child Garden." Do we who

FLAME TREE BRANCH

yearly revel in their wonderful blaze let the fires of appreciation die within our breasts?

The Poinciana lights her hearth in May from a veritable heap of dry twigs and branches, for this is one of the few deciduous trees of Honolulu. In some varieties the new leaves (large and finely compound) leap out, like the color of drift-wood, together with the flaming flowers, but in others they wait until the whole tree-top, like a rounded hill in a cane-trash fire, has kindled the eye and imagination of the beholder for a considerable time. Then, like ashes in the grate, they but add a dull background to the glory of the tree. June, July, August, even September, seem to derive added warmth from this vivid exponent of color-gospel, but soon the established foliage alone remains, umbrageous and beautiful. Alone, no, for hanging from the branches are long, flat, scimitar-shaped seed-pods, turning from green to brown, until, when the leaves depart, they reign supreme during the "winter of our discontent."

The tree grows from seed with rapidity under favorable conditions, attaining a height of twenty feet in a few years. It may begin branching low, making an umbrella-like canopy that sometimes sweeps the ground.

There are some twenty-five varieties of Poinciana here, in some of which the flower, borne when the tree is still young, has the true color of flame and is well called the Flamboyant or Flame Tree; in others it has a white eye set in scarlet and suggests the title it bears otherwise, Royal Peacock Flower, while in the richest variety it has a deep blood-red that stains the ground like the veriest Cain for gore! To insure the best blooming the Poinciana should be disarmed of its "scimitars" long before blossom-time, that the strength of the tree may be conserved, since "beauty is its own excuse for being."

23

YELLOW POINCIANA

Peltophorum inerme

One of our finest shade trees is the so-called Yellow Poinciana, native in Ceylon, Malaya, and in Northern Australia. Differing in shape from the familiar Royal Poinciana, it is often more than fifty feet in height and reaches up and out large branches with thick foliage of doubly divided leaves. The tree often flowers twice in one year, its large clusters of deep yellow blooms being succeeded by equally handsome, mahogany-colored seed-pods. It is deservedly much planted.

GOLDEN SHOWER

Cassia fistula

Well-known to the commercial world is the Cassia family, famous for its yield of drugs.

The *Cassia fistula,* which in Honolulu is called Golden Shower (rarely Golden Glow) is the Laburnum of India where, as in the East and West Indies, it is native and is commonly known as the Pudding-Pipe Tree. The early Arabs knew this tree for its medicinal value, and the Bengalese use the bark for tans and drugs and the pulp of the fruit both as a purging medicine and also as a flavor for tobacco in their smoking mixtures. These people use, also, the hard wood of the tree for carts and agricultural implements, for this Cassia is common from the Himalayas to Ceylon.

The Golden Shower has ornamented Honolulu gardens for perhaps forty odd years, but every year increases its popularity and that rightly. Its reproduction is from seed and the seeds are borne in separate-walled cells of long, straight, cylindrical, black pods, which, like the pods of the *Poinciana regia,* should be picked from the tree when ripe to conserve strength for the next crop of blossoms.

A height of some thirty feet is attained by the tree with a fair rapidity, but it blossoms when still a shrub in stature.

GOLDEN SHOWER SPRAY

The pinnate leaves measure twenty inches in length, each leaflet being the size of an orange leaf. Glossy and of a rich shade of green, the leaves bear a part in the display of the flowers.

The flowers, fragrant and borne in "long, lax racemes" are a translucent yellow, and from May to October hang from the lustrous green of the tree like etherealized grapes of pale amber, or a swarm of golden bees.

Pensacola Street bordered by these trees is a living

monument to the old resident who planted and tended the young saplings, and thus prepared for those she left at her passing a street of gold.

PINK SHOWERS

Cassia grandis

The *Cassia grandis*, a native of South America, taller and slenderer than its Indian sisters *Cassia fistula* and *Cassia nodosa*, and of rough bark and leaf, flings skyward in March long sprays of old-rose buds, enswathed in mist-like grey wrappings, that yield as the buds unfold to the shell-pink flowers whose days are numbered.

Cassia nodosa

April, bidding farewell to the swift-passing *Cassia grandis*, welcomes the *Cassia nodosa* as the promised May-queen. It is called Pink Shower and Pink-and-White Shower, as we have two close-kin varieties, and also called through some botanical misadventure by the incorrect and inelegant name, *Cathartacarpus*. *Cassia nodosa*, a rapid grower from seed (held in a pod very like that of the Golden Shower) has a huge leaf pinnately made up of small pretty leaflets. It is graceful in structure if pruned intelligently, otherwise becoming scraggy, and is each year in greater favor. It may soon rival the Cherry Tree of Japan as an attraction for trans-Pacific travel. It has a fragrance all its own, but its exquisite shading of color on the long lovely bough makes it, more than any other tree outside the temperate zone, resemble the Apple, and brings homesick longings and flights of romantic memory to many a human transplanted to the tropics. In the month of May the trees stand in fair procession along

GOLDEN SHOWER (Cassia fistola)

suburban streets, arrayed as though celebrating the bridal of earth and heaven.

Porto Rican Candelabra

Cassia alata

Whether or not Porto Rico ever saw this beautiful garden plant that commonly bears its name, this native of India holds its large pinnate leaves and erect racemes of golden blossoms, each a gem of nature's carving, like stately branched candlesticks. This spring-blooming shrub is short-lived but is easily replaced from the plentiful seeds in the interestingly winged pods from which comes the *alata* of its botanical name.

Kolomona

Cassia glauca

Sometimes in parks and gardens and more often along country roads, in Manoa and Nuuanu valleys or on the round-the-island drive, glows the cheerful Kolomona. Its clusters of round yellow flowers, the thin brown pods and pinnate leaves that fold their smooth, blunt, grey-backed leaflets at night make the slender little tree joyous and friendly to meet. A very early importation, though now gone wild, its name given by the Hawaiians, Kolomona, suggests that it may have illustrated a missionary lesson on "even Solomon in all his glory."

Cassia laevigata

More shrub- or vine-like, this close kin of the foregoing Cassia differs principally in having pods round instead of flat.

27

Peacock Flower or Pride of Barbadoes

Caesalpinia pulcherrima

Devoted to many of our indigenous trees from youthful association or old time legend, how ignorant we are of the uses and meanings of many of our imported plants. Two gay shrubs, familiarly planted, wear throughout the year dainty flower clusters terminating the spiny branches that show the subdivided leaf and slender pod characteristic of their family. From the scarlet or yellow blossoms spring aigrette-like filaments of staminate tubes, as if bright butter-flies were perched for flight. We call the shrubs Pride of Barbadoes, and lo, they are not only the pride of humans, but, in India are sacred to the God Shiva.

Wiliwili

Erythrina monosperma

This genus is declared to be difficult to classify but that need not bother us as only one species, the one we are considering, is native here and but few have been introduced. The range of the genus is from the Himalayas to the woods of West Africa, including the tropical regions of Australia and the Americas. The species native to our islands is found also in the Southern Pacific. It is rarely seen in the city but thrives in the dry portions of several of the islands.

Its light-colored bark covers the lightest-weight wood of Hawaii, which, cork-like, has had, always, a distinctive use in the "float log" of the outrigger canoe, being connected with the boat by bars of Hau. It is used also to make floats for the famous fishing nets and, in olden days, it furnished surfboards for little children.

Although unsymmetrical and a little uncouth in character, it has a comely leaf nearly heart-shaped and prettily veined and its orange-red flowers have an exotic and mysterious look, suggesting the tiger-claw jewelry worn by our court ladies fifty years ago. The Wiliwili is one of the few trees to drop its old leaves before the new appear. This is after the blooming time which varies. Mr. Rock gives Spring to July as the flowering season, but in North Kona we have found bloom in October, this, however, with leaves. The name *monosperma* is inaccurate as the curved pods, one and one half to three inches long, hold from one to several seeds. These have given their name, Wiliwili, to all red seeds used in the making of leis.

Coral Tree —— Wiliwili Haole

Erythrina indica

This importation is one of the most vivid trees and is called by several names: Tiger-claw, Foreign Wiliwili, Indian Wiliwili. It is an Indian species but is much at home here and in February is a striking sight in different parts of Honolulu with its bare white limbs and dense clusters of scarlet flowers, very like those of the native Wiliwili. The tree grows quickly to its height of forty-five feet. It wears prickles on its branches and before blooming drops its pretty, almost triangular leaves arranged in groups of three.

We remember seeing in Australia a grove of these trees blazing into the bluest of skies and, under their red canopies, a huge flock of snow-white chickens.

29

False Wiliwili

Adenathera pavonina

How one hates to call a plant false-anything. It must be a true-something! This one seems too slight and agreeable a tree-friend to bear any stigma. Its other appellations, Red Wood and Red Sandalwood, are borrowed and not real. In India it makes an honest dye but its wood is a substitute for real Red Sandalwood and even that is not sandalwood! The tree grows rather rapidly to a height of twenty feet or so, and, except for a short season, wears leaves twice divided and having eventual leaflets about the size of Monkeypod leaflets, smooth and a bluish green. One never notices the yellowish flowers but children eagerly await the clusters of brown pods that split and curl away back, showing their yellow linings and dropping their scarlet seeds. "Let us make a lei," yes, but call it by some pretty name not false! *Pavonina* is not so bad!

Elephant's Ear

Enterolobium cyclocarpum

Some people follow a rule of this sort; when ignorant of a flowering tree, call it a "Shower"; when in doubt as to a plant with large leaves, call it "Elephant's Ear"! This tall and wide spread tree is a native of Jamaica and Venezuela. It belongs to the "Shower" family but is not a Shower; has "elephant ears," but they are seed-pods and not leaves. Its pinnate leaves are subdivided into ultimate small leaflets. The small flowers are made up of numerous white stamens. The almost-circular seed-pods are shiny "wooden elephant ears." Some people are fond of this tree; some are not. There is a number of large specimens in public parks. Two especially fine examples may be seen on Tenth Avenue and one in the grounds of the Board of Agriculture on Keeaumoku Street.

THE BIGNONIA FAMILY

ORANGE TRUMPET VINE —— Huapala

Bignonia (renamed *Pyrostegia*) *venusta*

Mr. Bryan gives the Hawaiian name of this vine as *Hulupala* signifying auburn, and surely auburn-tressed, of a very red-headed variety, is this fair daughter of nature but it is more commonly spoken as *Huapala* or Sweetheart Vine. The visitor from a cold climate declares that Honolulu hearth fires are on the top of the veranda or arbor, or even set the whole roof ablaze, and his heart glows at the showy spectacle offered by the *Bignonia venusta*. Because difficult to use as house decoration on account of its propensity to fade immediately upon cutting, this plant stimulates one housewife to try complete immersion of sprays for an hour, her treatment of cut Golden Shower, while another recommends a hot bath such as she gives Heliotrope; and another chars the ends of the stems as she does those of Poinsettia. But *Bignonia venusta* is a burning bush for only two or three months at the first of the year and during that time with unsurpassed virility is throwing out a wilderness of lusty-tendrilled branches that grow with all speed. The leaves under the flowers are a glossy, bright green and make the vine an attractive house-or-arbor-or-fence-climber throughout the year. The flower has the characteristic

31

tubular form of the Bignonia family, one side of the united corolla being depressed and the edge cut in curved scallops. It is a honey-holder. The vine is readily propagated from shoots springing from the widespread roots. It is long-lived, and the girth of an old vine may measure ten inches in diameter.

Hug-Me-Tight

Bignonia unguis cati (formerly *tweediana*)

This, the Cat's Claw Climber, usually called Hug-Me-Tight, is perhaps the favorite of all the Bignonias in Honolulu. By means of its numerous tiny claws it rapidly mantels stone or wooden fences or encircles lofty trees, its thread-like stems swelling with age till they resemble fearful serpents writhing about the tree to its eventual strangulation. From high branches this vine lets fall curtains of foliage that spread from bough to bough and often from tree to tree. Always attractive in glossy leaf, several times during the year it bursts into bloom, raining sheets of canary-colored blossoms that later spread a cloth of gold upon the lawn. If yellow is the color of joy, take your fill of delight in this vine!

Tecoma Vine

Bignonia jasminoides

This old resident of Honolulu is known also in Ceylon and should be a general favorite. From clusters of flowers having flattened tubes and spreading curved petals of pale pink and throats of mauve-maroon, it gives forth a delicate fragrance. The vine is sturdy and long-lived and the lightsome foliage resembles the leafage of the Cherokee Rose. It is a perennial bloomer.

32

Bignonia regina

This is one of the latest importations of the Bignonia family and is altogether delightful. Its fragrance is as pleasant as that of the Tecoma, a little stronger and more fruity. Its foliage is lighter and the bright pink flower, held in dainty clusters, is a deep, round cup, handsomely marked within.

JACARANDA

Jacaranda ovalifolia (or *mimosaefolia*)

The Jacaranda has a reputation of rank "among the one hundred best flowering trees or shrubs for subtropical regions." "Divinely tall and most divinely fair" this member of the Bignonia family is too infrequently seen in Honolulu, but it is the earliest tree to bloom and so each year leads the summer pageant of trees.

Southern California appreciates it but there is no record of its introduction into Florida. As its Brazilian name suggests, its native home is South America. In North America its name seems to have lost its Spanish pronunciation.

The Jacaranda grows rapidly, sending up a long slender trunk of grey that if given its way attains a considerable height before spreading its branches with their lacy, fern-like foliage. The coloring of its fragile blue flower clusters is exquisite. Standing under its lofty boughs on an April morning, one may easily imagine the sky, too nearly bending, has been caught among the fringing leaves or, fallen through, lies in lovely fragments—a sea of flowerets on the grass.

Sunshine Tree

(a Tecoma not yet specifically determined)

A tall, pale tree that sheds its palmate leaves before blooming stands on the *makai* side of School Street *ewa* of Nuuanu Avenue. Although imported by the famous botanist Dr. Hillebrand more than fifty years ago, it seems to have no adult descendants, hence because of its unique beauty it is an annual Mecca to lovers of trees or lovers of color when in February it becomes a marvel of transmuted sunshine. Only lately has the tree fruited. Now seedlings are for sale and one easily predicts a great new light for the city.

African Tulip or Fountain Tree

Spathodea campanulata

This is one of the newer importations in Honolulu and is fast winning popularity, being seen in many parts of the city. Its large, showy vermilion flowers are clustered on the ends of rich leafy branches. It seems to be in bloom throughout the year and strews the ground with brilliant fallen blossoms.

It is said that in Java the children make play-canoes of the boat-shaped capsules.

Calabash Tree

Crescentia cujute

A round, stiff tree about fifteen feet high, spreading its sometimes tangled branches horizontally, this Bignonia quickly discards its pale green flowers to concentrate attention on its astonishing fruit. Its flowers are really worth noticing, for their heavily crinkled tubes hold anthers exquisitely formed like fairy grey moths. Its odor and moisture, not attractive to humans, are probably otherwise translated by insects. The fertilized ovum, clinging by the shortest of stems to the rough bark of trunk or branch, swells to the size of a baby's head. It is a smooth green globe, most ornamental on the tree, and, capable of being bound into desired shapes while growing, takes a fine polish when matured and picked.

SAUSAGE TREE

Kigelia africana

The grounds of the University of Hawaii show a tree as grotesque as one can imagine, for this strange cousin of flowers so fair is still a Bignonia though known for its huge sausage-shaped fruit, fifteen to twenty inches long and three to four inches thick when fully grown, that succeed the handsome, magenta flowers. The tree is bare of leaves for a part of each year and is curious rather than attractive.

BOUGAINVILLEA FAMILY

"A monument more enduring than brass," because a living and developing thing, is that which, found in most tropical countries, bears the name of the eighteenth century navigator De Bougainville. Did he discover in some South American forest this unrivalled color-exhibit of nature in a single tone of its chromatic scale, or did some bevy of admirers place his name upon the most gorgeous product of Brazilian gardens?

35

Whatever his uncertain desert, his monument is world-famous.

Less than a dozen species of Bougainvillea are recognized, but, sun-lovers, and thriving in soils of varied sorts, they play, according to soil composition, water supply, and conditions of sun or shade, individual gradations in the gamut of color, purple, magenta, deep rose-red, brighter rose-red, brick-red-fading-to-tan, dull

BOUGAINVILLEA VINE

pink, white. The white is the only variety still a stranger to Honolulu, although the only pink, one recalls, is on a Keeaumoku Street dwelling. The purple is one of the oldest landmarks among imported plants.

A mammoth specimen of the last (*spectabilis*) with a trunk nine feet in circumference, supported on an iron trellis occupies what might be the space of a commodious three story house on grounds corner of King and Alapai Streets.

The Punahou School grounds hold arbors covered with the brick-red (*spectabilis var. lateritia*).

In the Church Garden, corner of Punahou and Beretania streets, the small-flowered magenta, a perennial bloomer (*spectabilis var. parviflora*) has climbed through an old Algaroba tree to a height of forty feet

BOUGAINVILLEA DETAIL

and transmits the sunlight as through a many-mullioned, stained-glass window. This magenta variety which has so far been the most commonly cultivated is strident in note and unless adjacent plants are carefully chosen for color combination, (abundant green foliage, grey trunks of Palms, white Oleander or pale yellow Bignonia, for instance) is unutterably harsh in

37

the landscape. The red varieties are placed with less difficulty, particularly the deep rose-red which neighbors well with Oleander, pink Hibiscus, blue Plumbago and other flowers of gentle hues. The rose-red *glabra,* moreover, differs from the rest as suggested by the name, in being glabrous throughout branch, leaf and bract. It seems a higher or more civilized type of plant. A still brighter red lately introduced may eclipse all the rest in popularity.

Although provided with strong hooks for climbing, the Bougainvillea is nothing loth to assume a shrublike aspect and unless bridled will prove a headstrong runaway. Tamed as a fence-cover, it is, because of its density and thorny character, an impenetrable barrier.

The leaf, evergreen and dark, makes the plant attractive during its few months entirely without bloom.

The brilliant and striking colors of the Bougainvillea belong not to the true flower at all but to the bracts, leaf-like in shape and veining, that almost completely hide the small, inconspicuous, tubular blossoms.

The plant is propagated from cuttings of young shoots laid in sandy soil and preferably rooted before being severed from the parent vine.

BUCKWHEAT FAMILY

Mexican Creeper

Antigonon leptopus

This charming vine, a native of Mexico and Central America, is one of the early importations and deserves to be more commonly cultivated. A perennial bloomer, with dainty clusters of small blossoms, it flowers freely whether running upon the ground or low fence or given opportunity to fling its bright beauty among the tree tops.

The variety *albus,* introduced recently, now completes the gamut of color from deep cherry through rose and pink to white and there are self-crossings and reversions to type.

The vine is easily propagated from seed or from tubers springing up about the parent plant. It is found in many tropical countries and in parts of the Far East is called Honolulu Vine. Since both blossom and leaf are heart shaped, the latter curved over and heavily netted with veins, and since the blushing flower-racemes end in clinging tendrils by which the vine ascends, its sentimental Spanish name, *Cadena del Amor,* Chain of Love, seems appropriate and best.

CACTUS FAMILY

PRICKLY PEAR —— Panini

Opuntia tuna

It seems strange that this wall-like Mexican plant, gifted not only with thorns obvious but with thorns insidious, enemies in ambush that cling and pervade and inflame, should have been introduced here where our islands are so free from poisons, animal and vegetable, knowing not snake nor Poison Ivy nor Poison Oak. However, seizing vast tracts of our arid lands the Prickly Pear has in time of drought furnished life-saving food and moisture to cattle. These animals manage the leaves cannily, rolling them on the ground to divest them of their worst spines. The blue-green substance of this unique growth (one fan-like leaf superimposed at an angle on another, as in a Japanest juggling trick, and its brilliant flowers making way for the blue-blood fruit, agreeably edible if patiently and carefully peeled for dethroning) is picturesque to a degree and plays its uncouth part in nature's subtle drama.

Night-blooming Cereus

Cereus triangularis

The Night-blooming Cereus, a native of Mexico, was brought to Honolulu before 1840. Since it thrives in dry places and without care, it might long before now have become a rival of the Prickly Pear (*Opuntia tuna*). Doubtless in a few decades, owing to Honolulu's increasing interest in planting, many a desert place will have been transformed by this mysterious plant.

The blossom stands stemless on the angled branch of the sharp-spined, creeping cactus. It is six or seven inches across and about twelve inches long and is inclosed at the base by scale-like bracts from which rise green-gold sepals, long, slender, and curving entirely over the glistening white petals. These are numerous and overlapping and inclose about nine hundred delicately quivering golden stamens surrounding the long, thick style with spider-shaped stigma. The odor is heavy, almost rank.

In Honolulu the fruit rarely forms. It is a rather palatable, brilliant red globe of pulp holding a few seeds. The seeds, however, are disregarded for reproduction as the plant grows from self-rooting sections of branches.

Little use is made of this variety save by the Chinese who gather the flowers for food and medicine.

A few other of the many Night-bloomers are of more recent importation. One, the Queen Cactus (*Phyllocactus sp.*) is a prized tree-climber, flat-branched and thin in structure, with flowers hanging like graceful pipes, smaller, finer in every way, including perfume,

NIGHT-BLOOMING CEREUS

than the *Cereus triangularis,* and with sepals rosy instead of golden. This deserves to be a garden favorite, for the flowers, alluring when swinging in the wind and shifting night light, are as exquisite as Waterlilies, which they resemble, and, hanging from wall-vase or laid on a mirror, make unsurpassed evening house decorations.

The mecca of all Honolulu's vegetation is the mile of

stone wall bounding the Punahou Campus and covered with the *Cereus triangularis*. Sluggish and inert throughout the year, self-bewitched into a heap of spiny, thick sea-serpents struggling through the entangled mass of themselves, waving thread-like roots that feel vaguely for foothold, in summer the nightbloomer asserts its queenly place in the floral kingdom. Several nights each month from June to October when in the moonlight pilgrimages are made to this shrine of beauty, ten thousand flower-cups at once are held aloft —earth's elevation of the Host—smiled upon by the light of another world.

CASUARINA FAMILY

Ironwood

Casuarina equisitifolia

A stranger is sure to ask the name of the grey-green, lofty, drooping trees bordering the road through Kapiolani Park, which, though unrelated, suggest the Conifers. The specific name *equisitifolia* is well given, as the long, pendent pine needles which serve the tree instead of leaves, might well be manes and tails of horses of the imagination. To those who, in our everlasting summer, yearn for the soughing of northern pines, these trees sing a sweet and minor song. They also fling down soft matting needles and little brown near-cones as pretty toys for children.

A second species, *Casuarina quadrivalis*, has been planted by the Forestry Department on the near side the Nuuanu Pali.

Of large proportions and spread, the Ironwood also

lends itself to artificial trimming into hedges and grotesque clipped ornaments as shown in Japanese gardens. It furnishes excellent firewood and is useful as windbreak, but is often planted for its beauty in single uncrowded specimens. Old residents drive through Kapiolani Park with thankfulness that a landscape gardener, imported to "do over" the park, was not allowed his whim to destroy the avenue of Ironwoods and to substitute other trees, but was himself removed.

COFFEE FAMILY

COFFEE

Coffea arabica

Almost as early as the first missionaries reached Hawaii, came a Frenchman with the seeds of Arabian coffee and, from the small plantation started by him in Manoa Valley, has sprung the Kona Coffee industry, ranking fifth among the island industries and bearing the name of the district of its greatest and best production. If is is not possible to visit Kona on the "Big Island" at harvest time, there to delight the eye with the tangled groves of slender, shrub-like trees, their pendent branches hanging "heavy, heavy over your head" with long rows of scarlet and crimson berries like beads sewn close to the stem, a small grove of coffee, planted some thirty odd years ago, may be seen on the Tantalus Drive.

The small fragrant white flowers, like long threaded leis, give place to the fruit in late summer, and in late October the bright berry calls "open my heart and you will see hid inside of it" those mystic twin beans, pale green, covered with a thin sweet pulp (that will attract your children rather than yourself) and under that a tight skin that must be removed ere from the dried and roasted product you scent the spice of Araby the blest.

One wonders that this most attractive tree is not more planted in gardens for aesthetic reasons if not for the fun, and incidentally the work, of serving one's own table.

If the season is long enough the coffee boughs present rubies, gems of orient, as if the Magi's Christmas offering.

Ixora

Ixora macrothyrsa

Very few of the exceedingly numerous family *Rubiaceae* have come to Hawaii, but beside the Coffee already mentioned is the *Ixora macrothyrsa,* one of the showiest shrubs. Like the Coffee, it has heavy, rich green pointed leaves, but its flower which is minute is combined into large clusters, scarlet usually (although there is a variety of salmon pink) in almost spherical bunches of brilliant beauty. There is a newly introduced white that must be cherished. Every garden may have this plant for it is easily cultivated from cuttings. Since it blooms throughout the year the scarlet flowers may be counted on among the contributors to Christmas decorations.

COTTON TREE FAMILY

Few species of the many in this family known throughout tropical countries are found here.

BOMBAX
Bombax ellipticum

This one holds such rare and vivid beauty as to call much attention. The only specimen known to the writer is in the grounds of the Queen's hospital but it is a shrine for visitors in March, the month of its bloom, for the flowers are enough to make the tree, which is short, sparse and too long bare of leaves, forgive Nature for her lack of many gifts in the glory of this one. The blossom springs from an audibly exploding long brown bud and the petals, immediately curling over backwards, display their cream satin linings and make room for a mass of long brilliant pink stamens, a shower of rosiness as if the dawn of a day were concentrated in a flower tassel.

SILK COTTON TREE or KAPOK
Ceiba pentandra

COTTON TREE
Bombax ceiba

Both these trees are tall and columnar, spread their branches horizontally and divide their deciduous leaves digitately. The Bombax ceiba is much the larger and finer of the two, has its bark well spined, like armor, and draws up its knees, so to speak, having buttresses about it some seven feet in height and running out above ground fifty or sixty feet—witness the one on Keeaumoku Street near King Street, in the grounds of the Board of Agriculture. The flowering and fruiting of this tree are somewhat uncertain in Honolulu. In other countries the floss contained in the capsule is of commercial value. Ceiba pentandra, tall, handsome but slightly buttressed, stands near King Street in the Capitol grounds.

CUSTARD-APPLE FAMILY

Ylang ylang

Cananga odorata

The very name Ylang ylang suggests mystery and is the essence of things remote and exotic. More com-

YLANG YLANG

mon than the Ylang ylang tree named above is the shrub, *Artabotrys uncinnatus,* which seems like an unsupported vine with bowed head and many shiny leaves that hide the green, drooping flowers and fruit. Its pervasive perfume is haunting.

CYCAS FAMILY

Sago Palms (so-called)

Cycas revoluta

Our two so-called Sago Palms are not Palms and do not yield sago, which facts suggest that we often seem to live in a land of make-believe!

SO-CALLED SAGO PALM
(*Cycas revoluta*)

The *Cycas revoluta* is as often planted in tubs as in the ground, and, not more than three feet high, wears above its stout trunk a heavy crown of leaves that look like fern fronds made of thin wood and painted

dark green. This plant, a native of China, is not supposed to branch. (See if you can't find exceptions. It
would be in character!)

Cycas circinalis

This Cycas, which grows wild in Guam and in
Ceylon, is much planted in Honolulu. Growing eventually to fifteen or twenty feet, this Palm-like tree
wears a crown of exceedingly graceful ferny leaves
sometimes six or seven feet long. If the top of the
trunk is cut the tree will branch but it is finer if it does
not. Its cone, on a much larger scale than that of
the first-named variety, furnishes a starch difficult to
use because of poisonous factors and in shape and color
suggests an enlarged and lengthened pineapple-cheese.

When the scientists tell us that the Cycas family is
older than that of the Conifers, our minds are lost in
that jungle of beauty that was when the world was
young and these plants, with the Ferns, were monarchs
of the forests.

EUPHORBIA FAMILY

Kukui

Aleurites molcuccana

Indigenous! What does that mean? Here are trees
long antedating the first footprint of the discovering
human, but identical with trees elsewhere on the globe.
Birds, winds, waves—can these account for all indigenous plants? To this group of trees wrapped in the
mists of prehistoric days belongs the Candle-nut,

49

supposedly of Malay and called native in Hawaii also. It is named Kukui by the Hawaiian, and since the time when he strung its oily nuts on the strong mid-rib of a palm-leaf for his fragrant torch, he has given to each later light, candle, whale-oil, kerosene, or electric, lamp, the same appellation. By a rather pretty fancy the Hawaiian Light-House Tender bears the name "Kukui."

A marked feature observed from a ship nearing Honolulu is the surprising variety of greens in the foliage. This is not wondered at when one names over the world-wide immigrants that compose the vegetation of the city, but on the wooded slopes back of Honolulu it is the Kukui groves, silver as olives, that make light in the darkness of Koa, like tracts of sunshine breaking through cloud-shadows on dusky mountain ranges. It is the old Kukui that is silvery, for the leaves of this tree in youth and age are so unlike as to be mistaken for different varieties. The sapling's leaf is rich green, variable in shape but resembling that of Maple, broad, and having several points. Later the central point lengthens, leaving only two short points at the back and a white bloom overspreads the entire leaf as if to tone in with the creamy color of the flowers.

The flowers, lilac-like, but differing in fragrance and also in position, stand at the tips of the twigs like clusters of fairy lights.

The nut has an exceedingly hard shell, grooved in symmetrical curves. This, when polished, has for many years been used for ornaments by jewellers and curio dealers. Honolulu makes no commercial use of the Kukui, although the nut yields sixty percent of valuable oil. By the Hawaiian the nut is much used.

The oily meat of the nut has a fine flavor when roasted and is always an accessory at a *luau* (feast). The green nut offers a vigorous carthartic, to be used with great caution. The sap from the leaves has astringent and healing properties and makes a convenient first-aid remedy for wounds. A tattooing ink was made from the tree when that ornamentation was in fashion.

KUKUI LEAVES, FRUIT AND FLOWERS

In the mountains and valleys new forests are constantly springing from the ground strewn with nuts in their rotting husks half-embedded in loam. This is well, for the Kukui, comely in form and foliage and attaining a height of sixty feet or more, is unenduring because of its structure of soft wood. Although easy to cultivate and transplant and well adapted to different altitudes, growing luxuriously if given shade for a few years, there are few Kukui trees in parks and gardens of Honolulu.

On Kauai, the "Garden Isle," stands a grove of noble Kukui trees famed as the place of a great evangelistic revival in early mission days. Did, perhaps those simple, poet-souled natives associate the light of religious inspiration glowing in the face of the Missionary Father with their torch-bearing Kukui?

CROTONS

The so-called Crotons, scheduled botanically as *Codiaeums,* give us a touch of autumn all the year round. Planted in many gardens as single varieties, perhaps the Crotons are nowhere more attractively displayed than on the right hand side of Kalakaua Avenue a short distance from King Street, and again on Diamond Head Drive. In one short hedge are all the colors of a New England fall, whether of Maple, Birch, Beech, Elm or Oak. Like almost all foliage plants these shrubs receive only nominal flowers from the even hand of nature, but the leaves are widely variegated in shape, arrangement and combination of color and in intensity and number of tints.

COLEUS

This shrub, broader of leaf than the Croton, though as variegated as may be, is usually seen in shades of red. It glows in a mass at the first turn of the Makiki Heights road and makes a notable hedge on the Diamond Head Drive. It greatly attracts the average tourist but is less in favor with those planting new gardens as its color, rich and conspicuous, is not always harmonious.

Pink and White Bush

Phyllanthus roseopictus

A favorite member of the Euphorbia family, called by Mr. Rock a horticultural variety of the *Phyllanthus nivosus,* the "snow bush," is a dainty shrub or hedge plant sometimes mistaken at a distance for a mass of rosy flowers from its flecked pink and white leaves. Its scientific name at first seems a little overdone but when one is used to it, it seems to fit the painted foliage well.

Poinsettia

Euphorbia pulcherrima

This plant which of late years has rivalled the English Holly in its place upon Christmas cards and, planted in pots, fills the windows of florist shops as symbols of Christmas cheer, is even more at home in our sub-tropical land than in California and, planted in the ground, may grow as high as the house.

In order to obtain the most abundant flowering for the holiday season the shrubs should be cut back with apparent ruthlessness, for they may still be in bloom, during the month of May. Cuttings may then be planted in containers for house decoration, fertilization offered, and nature will do her part in producing symmetrical and abundant growth.

The so-called flowers are really true leaves, long-pointed and veined in scarlet disguise, grouped in whorl-like pattern,—gay banners needed, perhaps, in the scheme of reproduction to indicate the whereabouts of the tiny, obscure flowers. Hybridizations of cream-white and salmon-pink are new introductions.

The sap of the Poinsettia is a thick, milky juice almost as adhesive as collodion when it dries. Unless the stalks are charred or dipped into boiling water immediately upon cutting they droop beyond use for decoration.

In our childhood we were warned against the poisonous properties of the Poinsettia but it is now planted everywhere and one does not hear of disaster.

CROWN OF THORNS

Euphorbia splendens

Well, though cruelly, named is this Euphorbia whose leafless, milky stem is crowded with sharp slender thorns and whose scarlet flowers in almost constant bloom are hardly larger than drops of blood. It is used as an ornamental pot plant, sometimes trimmed into baskets or other forms, and is also planted as a low, ornamental and impenetrable hedge.

HAIRY NETTLE

Acalypha hispida

The literal translation of the name of this plant in no way suggests the garden ornament it is with long crimson catkins adorning its leafy foliage in its seasons of bloom.

CASTOR OIL TREE

Ricinus communis

The Castor Oil, perhaps one of our most striking wayside plants, was an early arrival in Hawaii but is little esteemed as a foliage plant, although some handsome varieties are noted in mainland gardens. It grows freely in weed-like luxuriance along country roads. No use is made of it commercially even though besides its oil it would offer its leaves for silk-worm culture. Children, not minding its rank odor, enjoy using the large palmate leaves as parasols.

FLY-CATCHING FAMILY

MAY-BASKET VINE

Aristolochia elegans

This is a quick-growing vine with small heart-shaped leaf and deep-throated, large-vestibuled flower. In color and marking the flower is like a dark purple-brown Indian print. Holding a wind bag, it may be inverted to float as a duck for a child's plaything. The seed-vessel, of brown paper-like texture, splits part way down and flares, each point being held to the stem by a separate "wire," making a fairy-like may-basket big enough to hold Heliotrope, Forgetmenot, or Crown of Thorns blossoms.

GINGER FAMILY

A deeply refreshing, aromatic quality pervades the whole fabric of this family, sometimes hot and spicy as in the edible roots of the Zingiber, sometimes almost overpowering as in the perfume of the Hedychiums, or both stimulating and soothing as in the pungent quality of Alpinia leaves. "Beauty of form and grace of vesture" have they all, and varied color.

YELLOW GINGER, APE AND BANANA

Chinese Ginger

Zingiber officinalis

This species was formerly but little cultivated here, its "hands" of flat dried root for curry coming from China, as the succulent preserve in the time-honored ginger-jar still comes. But increasing favor has followed the island-planting of ginger the past two decades and already the "Hawaiian Dry" ginger-ale is making a name for the local growth.

Hawaiian Ginger —— Awapuhi

Zingiber zerumbet

Throughout the woods this short-stalked plant is a friend to the warm and thirsty tramper. Dying down for a few months of winter rest it springs refreshed and offers bright red, fleshy "cones" of bracts, which guard but few and insignificant pale yellow flowers, and hold a draught for a parched throat or a shampoo for a hot head.

Yellow Ginger

Hedychium flavum

The group of Hedychiums is called elsewhere by various attractive names, Ginger Lily, Butterfly Lily, Garland Flower, all of which we who so love our lei flowers can appreciate. This Yellow Ginger, long gone wild beside water-courses in Nuuanu and other valleys, grows in great masses of tall-leaved stems and every summer bears plentiful clusters of corn-yellow flowers shaped like butterflies and springing from "cones" of green bracts. Those initiated into the mysteries open the buds and string them into leis which burgeon forth in full flower and heavy scent.

White Ginger

Hedychium coronarium

We should surely call "crowned" this exquisite daughter of nature that makes true the translation of her name Hedychium, "sweet snow." Not so wild nor so sturdy as the Yellow Ginger, differing in leaf and root, its resembling flower, more refined, is more alluring. Glistening, orchid-like yet more human, it is intensely fragrant and appeals as with ethereal yet subtle passion.

YELLOW GINGER

KAHILI GINGER

Hedychium gardnerianum

This plant received its name on sight when Mrs. Isenberg of Kauai brought it from its home in Singapore to Hawaii. Suggestive of the *kahili*, beloved token of royalty, dainty in structure and a beautiful yellow in color, it is sure to claim Hawaiian affection.

Pink Porcelain Ginger

Alpinia nutans

Much larger and heavier in leaf and stem than the foregoing Gingers, this species grows in huge clumps or may be planted as a leafy screen in place of a more formal hedge. The flowers covered by bracts of palest pink and tipped at their sharp ends with deep rose,

PINK PORCELAIN GINGER

seemingly made of enamel or porcelain, curve away from the protecting sheath, that looks as if made of thinnest sandalwood, and droop in graceful pointed racemes. Not all the buds open, but those that do, disclose a flower with one elaborately painted petal, dark shades of red and yellow in fine pattern setting off the jewel-like anthers and pistil. The plant is much used for decoration, tall stalks filling large jars, or the flower racemes, without leaves, laid in low vessels to rest upon a table.

59

Red Ginger

Alpinia samoensis

The Red Ginger, brought within the last two decades from Samoa or Fiji or both, is a favorite with Hawaiians and is much planted about houses, almost filling some door yards. Its heavy shrubbiness is like that of the *Alpinia nutans* although the leaf is different in shape and texture. Its flower is very different. An erect "cone" of bright dark red bracts which cover the inconspicuous flowers, nurtures adventitious buds also, which strike out from their gay cradles as full-leaved plants and even develop roots in the air. These sturdy urchins are all ready for planting in the ground to "carry on" the glory of the family.

Giant Gingers

Phaeomeria speciosa

Perhaps as much as any plant the Giant Ginger of Mauritius or of Java has been given different names and assigned to various branches of the Ginger family, *Amomum, Elletaria,* etc. Two fine varieties are to be seen in Honolulu. One has heads of compact yellow blossoms in shiny scarlet bracts with imposing involucres or outer frills, thrust up between towering bronze-backed leaves to a height of fifteen feet. Another, very like it but smaller and with paler green leaves, has heads of pink color and a surface as of glazed wax. These on first sight must have seemed to the Hawaiian like frozen torches or glorified *tabu* sticks.

GRAPE FAMILY

Isabella Grape

Vitis labrusca

The only Grape grown locally is the Isabella, with blue-black, medium-sized grapes in tightly compressed bunches and silver-lined leaves too pretty to be the prey of the grasshopper. If one is bothered by the acidity of the rather thick skin, grape juice, sherbet, jelly or jam will serve him an uncriticised delicacy. The name is haunting and one thanks our Latin residents, who are its chief cultivators, imagining that they, setting forth as laborers on their lengthy overseas trip to Hawaii half a century ago, brought with them the fruit named for her who blessed the adventures of Columbus! Undoubtedly, however, that wonderful Vancouver some ninety years earlier brought grape seeds in his pocket as a gift to the great Kamehameha! The Isabella is close kin of the Concord Grape in New England.

GRASS FAMILY

Bamboo Grass

Gynerium saccharoides

Not a member of the Bamboo family but of the Grass family, is the tall jointed Bamboo Grass that bears striped ribbon-like leaves varying in color from white through yellow to green, often handsomely striped. Its stalks though fragile are used in Italy for basketry and here may be made into pretty fences or summer-houses where great strength is not required. It is native in Tropical America.

OTHER GRASSES

The Pampas Grass (*Gynerium argenteum*) with its elegant plumes resembling those of Sugarcane, only more ornamental, is the most conspicuous among the cultivated Grasses.

The Egyptian Papyrus (*Cyperus Papyrus*) very tall, green and slender with filiform bunches of "leaflets" for heads is most attractive when planted beside pools or Lily ponds. From strips of the pith in the stem pressed together one of the earliest forms of paper was made. According to Pliny the fluffy heads were useless except as they adorned the statues of the gods.

Akin to this and much more planted is the Umbrella Grass (*Cyperus alternifolius*) recognized from its descriptive common name. Growing wild along streams is the "Job's Tears" plant (*Coix Lachryma-Jobi*). It produces hard grey "tears" that are strung into leis.

Round Top, or Ualakaa, a hill back of Honolulu is now tinged with pink a considerable part of the time, sometimes suggesting rosy snow banks and all because of Red Top (*Tricholaena rosea*), a fodder grass introduced on Maui and escaped to Oahu.

The rough-leaved silvery Lemon Grass (*Andropogon schoenanthus*) is an old garden favorite, growing in thick tufts of narrow, pointed, and very fragrant leaves.

Island lawns are usually planted (not sown) with the Bermuda Grass (*Cynodon dactylon*) called by the

Hawaiians *Manienie* in honor of Don Marin the Spaniard who so interested himself in bringing plants more than a century and a quarter ago. Set out in chopped pieces, the runners quickly make a fine matted surface, particularly if exposed to strong sunlight and given soil with enough sand for good drainage. Too much watering brings the Nut Grass (*Kyllinga monocephala*) which is practically ineradicable but is often smothered by a planting of *Buffalo* Grass (*Senotaphrum secundatum*). This grass, although coarse, thrives in shade too dense for other grasses and, running only on the surface, is easily kept in check.

GREVILLEA FAMILY

Silky or Silver Oak

Grevillea robusta

Another native of Queensland, and of the same great family as the Macadamian Nut to be described, although very different in every way as far as the layman can observe, is the *Grevillea robusta*. Not too prepossessing in its youth, with rough bark and lack of grace, it may attain a height of from eighty to one hundred feet and a largeness that is impressive. Good specimens may be seen on the *mauka* boundary of the premises occupied by the Board of Agriculture. Its foliage is particularly noticeable, fern-like in a diversified pattern of incision and with its upper dark surface in sharp contrast to the under side of silver silk. It has many desirable qualities, being hardy, quick of growth, tenacious of life, almost regardless of drought

63

or other untoward conditions. Its orange-yellow flowers are unusual, being held like compressed feathers that at a signal from Mother Nature spring out in fluffy sprays. They, together with the red flowers of the smaller variety, *Grevillea banksii,* have come of late to be used by florists in attractive arrangements. *Grevillea robusta* is planted as wind-break on some parts of the islands and, though used a little for street-planting, seems less well adapted than others for ornamental purposes. Its wood has a commercial value in Australia.

MACADAMIAN NUT

Macadamia ternifolia

Among the introductions of latter years are a few varieties of nut. These must be suited to a sub-tropic zone and not dependent upon frost. Perhaps the best of these is the Macadamian Nut, sometimes called the Queensland Nut from its native habitat. This tree has of late been much planted, notably at Nutridge Farm, a tract of Territorial land on the *ewa* side of Round Top, Ualakaa. Its fruit, a hard-shelled nut, sprung from small white flowers in long white tassels yields a kernel so delicious, raw or roasted, as to make everyone desire a tree in his garden. As, in Hawaii, it is eventually of medium size it may well be planted even in small yards. One should not be discouraged in waiting for the maturity of the tree for it habitually "sits still" as a tiny plant for about three years and then shoots up into a slim shrub somewhat resembling English Holly in its shapely, bright, thorn-edged leaves.

"Now all may have the flower for all have got the seed."

HELIOTROPE FAMILY

Kou

Cordia subcordata

The Kou, indigenous or prehistorically imported is in name and wood often confused even by the long resident, with the Koa to which it is in no way akin. The living Kou tree is now rarely seen and attains only about half its pristine size, being today not more than a large shrub. A few good specimens planted by Dr. James R. Judd are struggling with an insect pest at Kahala. Unlike the Koa in habitat as well as otherwise, the Kou is a sea-shore tree.

Its rough bark and shape of leaf suggest the Milo, to which it is not related. The flower, however, is very different, being small, tubular-flaring and orange in color. The seed is borne in a small nut.

The wood of the Kou is distinguished from the variously marked golden brown of the Koa by its very dark brown color holding large light patches. Formerly abundant, the Kou, was the favorite wood for the making of Hawaiian vessels, containers for food and washing bowls. (The Hawaiians daintily washed their fingers in a polished calabash before dipping into the common food receptacles.) Although it is often stated that Koa also was used for calabashes, the writer has been told that it was not so used because it would impart a flavor to the food.

Foreign Kou —— Kou Haole

Cordia sebestena

This tree much resembling the native Kou is too little planted to be called familiar.

A few indigenous creeping varieties of Heliotrope with blue or white flowers are found on sandy sea-coasts of our islands.

HENNA FAMILY

CREPE MYRTLE

Lagerstroemia indica

The Crepe Myrtle, despite its common name, is not a Myrtle. It is a native of China and an old resident of Honolulu but wears only one color, "Portuguese pink." The shrub is sometimes fifteen feet high and is always comely in form. During the summer months it is covered with the delicate crepey-textured flowers. One wonders why other shades and also the lovely white varieties cultivated in Maryland and otherwhere on the Mainland are not planted here.

HIBISCUS FAMILY

The Hibiscus has been chosen as the Territorial Flower of Hawaii. There are a few native species, two or three of them white, two red and one yellow. One variety, a cup of five ivory-white petals in a calyx of jade green and holding a ruby style adorned with amber anthers and tipped with a garnet velvet stigma, pervaded, also, by a delicate fragrance, holds a princely place among the indigenous flowers.

Its especial appropriateness as a symbol of the Territory lies in the hybridization of the Hibiscus into thousands of varieties that by their differing excellencies of shape, size, contour, endurance and marvel-

THE CHERILLA LOWREY
Hibiscus

lously varied colors suggest Hawaii's demonstration of her multi-racial yet homogeneous and happy community.

67

COMMON RED HIBISCUS

Hibiscus rosa-sinensis

The Common Red Hibiscus was one of the earliest introduced plants and, called the China Rose, was always then, as it is seldom now, grown as a large shrub. Its profuse bloom, brilliant color, and hardy thick growth of handsome foliage give it preëminence as a hedge plant in Honolulu.

CORAL HIBISCUS

Hibiscus schizopetalus

The Coral Hibiscus, drooping graceful, small-leaved branches hung with coral-colored flowers, their finely cut petal-lips curved back from the long pendent tongue of the staminal tube, stands twice the height of a man and makes a showy arbor.

ROSE-MALLOW

Hibiscus mutabilis

The changeable Rose-Mallow, sometimes fifteen feet high, bears the adjective Virgil assigned to woman, "mutabilis." Its charm, single or double, is its path of color from the white of morning through the blush of noon to the deep rose of evening when it disputes the poet's "as if a rose should shut and be a bud again," for it does!

ROSELLE

Hibiscus sabdariffa

An annual familiar in Southern California and in Florida is the Roselle,—playing a unique rôle in the family, that of jelly-producer. With no boast of her flower nor her palmate leaves, she offers her calyces, so fleshy and crimson they suggest that the jelly is nearly done. Try her gift and praise her!

Ilima

Sida spp

This "royal flower of Hawaii," savoring of princely days gone by, is the most modest of the Mallows and exists in several species of *Sida*. Its separate flowers,

ILIMA

yellow or orange, as delicate as chiffon, strung by the cunning hands of the Hawaiian into leis, are not only lovely in themselves but are symbolic of the choicest gift that can be made.

COTTON

Gossypium spp

Hawaii has two rare indigenous varieties of Cotton, Mao, with yellow flowers (*Gossypium tomentosum*), and Kokio, with reddish flowers (*Gossypium drynarioides*). It would be interesting for the Outdoor Circle to propagate the idea of their planting. Several cultivated varieties have long been known here, one of them dating back to the time of Kamehameha the Great.

The handsome three-lobed fringed calyx guards the acorn-like receptacle that finally bursts with a gush of snowy cotton and black seeds.

HOLLYHOCK

Althea rosea

In carefully selected horticultural varieties the Hollyhock deigns to inhabit our gardens and is as traditionally stately as those bordering the door-paths of our New England forbears.

HAU

Hibiscus tileaceus

One of the first trees to greet the overseas traveller is the Hau offering a shady nook at the larger of the beach hotels and at the smaller ones making the roof of the outdoor living room, *lanai*. Though in the private grounds of La Pietra on the slope of Diamond Head, where it is associated with Olive and Cypress, the Hau suggests the grape arbors of Italy, at Gray's Hotel or at Halekulani, where the same gnarled trunks invited children of fifty years ago to climb them, the character of the Hau is ruggedly Hawaiian, tropic, weird, its own. Follow if you will any branch as it leaves the trunk, scramble over the top of the mass growth with no more fear of falling through than on a spring bed, or weave your body through the thornless

HAU AND COCONUT TREES

interstices of branches, and eventually, like a knight seeking the Holy Grail, you may find yourself at your point of departure. Such a tangle as roofs the *lanai* at the seashore is intensified as it grows in the higher, moister zones and in its strange formations might offer a theme for the imagination of an Arthur Rackham.

Dense as is the growth, it is easy to clear, as much

of the wood is soft enough for a cane-knife. Its vitality is so great that fence posts cut from the thicket sometimes start new jungles. The lightness and softness of the wood is too swiftly ash-producing to make a satisfactory firewood, but is unrivalled in its use as crossbars for the outrigger canoe. In the eighties there was

HAU TREE

a fad for making hat-braid from its shavings. Failing their usual and better fibres, the Hawaiians sometimes used Hau bark for beating into *tapa* cloth. Like so many of the indigenous plants the Hau had its place in the *materia medica* of the Hawaiians. Its capsule fruit is disregarded for planting in favor of cuttings.

Added to its charm of green, silver-backed leaf and grateful shade, the Hau has a notable flower, somewhat characteristic of the huge Hibiscus family but having its own variation of being honey-holding, fragrant and golden-yellow today, tomorrow old-rose, and next day a closed scroll of dull mahogany at your feet.

Milo

Thespesia populnea

The Milo, having a nut resembling that of the Kukui, has a leaf and blossom so like that of the Hau as often to be mistaken for it. It has not however its unbridled tendency for making jungles but grows a straight trunk to perhaps forty feet with a two foot diameter, and is content with a circumscribed shade. Like the Hau it sheds its leaves, which also turn yellow and brown after falling so freely as to be called a dirty tree.

The Milo, is not found so high as the Hau, which, although a lowlander, will thrive at fifteen hundred feet. It is much less planted, but good specimens may be seen in various parts of town, in Manoa Valley, on Punahou Street and in the new planting about the Honolulu Academy of Arts on Beretania Street.

Its wood is hard, of a rich brown color and, taking a fine polish, was used like the Kou for calabashes. It is now hard to obtain.

LAUREL FAMILY

Avocado or Alligator Pear

Persea gratissima

A tree increasingly appreciated and planted is the Avocado, the name being corrupted from the Gua-

tamalan Aguacato, commonly called the Alligator
Pear, probably because the early importations had a
skin resembling an alligator hide in looks. Not only is
the fruit one of the best and most delicious of foods
but the tree itself is desirable, quick of growth, reaching from ten to forty feet in height, and having pleas-
ant-shading branches. The leaves are variously shaped,

AVOCADO PEAR

ovate to lanceolate and fall usually after the new
leaves are set and the tree is pale gold in its innumerable tiny blossoms. A native of tropical America, the
Avocado is one of the many plants for which the
Islands are indebted to their long ago benefactor, the
Spaniard, Don Marin. The varieties seem legion since
the tree does not come true from seed. The fruit is, in
general, pear shaped, ranging from long bottle necks

74

almost to spheres, graded from four to nine inches in length and weighing sometimes several pounds. The skin may differ in smoothness or other quality of texture, and in color may be green, mahoghany red, brown or purple. The flesh may be thin and stringy or thick and almost as rich as butter. The single seed differs in size and in degree of separateness from the surrounding flesh.

Today the careful fruitgrower depends upon budding or grafting from the finest varieties. Such trees produce fruit about four years after planting. By choosing varieties according to their season for fruiting, the table may be supplied the year around.

The Avocado appears upon the menu in many forms,—as the substance of a tomato-and-lemon-flavored cocktail, as a thickening for soup or French dressing, as a salad with or without combination, a sandwich filler, an excellent addition to scrambled egg, an accompaniment to curry, even as the body of an almond-flavored ice cream. In Ceylon this pear is called Soldiers' Butter. Variable in every characteristic and use, it may be called a Harlequin of fruits and withal a pleasure-giver.

Camphor Tree

Cinnamomum camphora

The Camphor tree, with small pointed leathery leaves which on being crushed emit a strong odor of camphor, is a handsome addition to a garden but does not always thrive in Honolulu and is not often seen. There is a fine group of old and noble trees at Kealia on Kauai. Although planted in many parts of the world almost the entire commercial supply comes from Formosa.

LILY FAMILY

Ki, Ti, or Lai

Cordyline terminalis

This interesting plant in variations is spread from India, through Australia, New Zealand and the islands of the Pacific. One cannot imagine an emigrant setting

KI PLANTS

forth on a canoe voyage of discovery without a supply of Ki, lest he find none in his new habitat, for what would take its place in thatching his roof, clothing his person, sandaling his feet, wrapping his food for cooking or for keeping clean and cool, covering table or floor, furnishing fly-brushes and brooms, binding wounds, giving beauty in leaf and flower, satisfaction in sweet roots to chew in hours of ruminating rest, strong liquor (*okolehao*) to distil? The plant grows wild in the woods and is cultivated in hedges or in clumps and is used decoratively, planted or cut. Purple and red species are seen in cultivation but the green,

KI LEAF AND FLOWER

with its annual bloom of creamy, palm-like, bee-sought blossoms set on chocolate colored stems among the long, rich, shiny leaves is a comforting joy. It would be no surprise to learn that the idea of the *kahili* as royal insignia sprang from these slender stems with their dignified leafy heads.

77

Yucca gloriosa

A favorite in Honolulu yards forty years ago but not often seen now, is the Spanish Bayonet that above its tall slender body bristling with leafy bayonets, wears a high helmet-shaped panicle of showy white flowers. With the introduction of Spanish types of houses and the development of more arid sections of Honolulu one expects to see the bayonets flash and the helmets glisten again.

Other Lilies

The very name of this family tempts one to wander among the numerous garden varieties, including the blue or white *Agapanthus umbellatus* and the beds of the yellow Day Lily (*Hemerocallis flava*) that have multiplied beyond reckoning the past few years, or to call attention to the Micronesian Lilies, long stalks of white spider-shaped flowers lighting up dark clumps of leaves head-high and more. But we have already stepped beyond bounds; the loam of our wandering retards our feet; the Iris family with all their hybrid Gladioli look askance; the Cannas, cousins of the Bananas and Gingers, are scarlet with annoyance and yellow with envy at having been passed by; we must draw our skirts from all enticing borders and keep to the shade of trees and vines.

MAGNOLIA FAMILY

Magnolia grandiflora

The Magnolia of Honolulu is disappointing to many visitors accustomed to the large umbrageous trees of the Southern States. What is lacking in quantity, however, is made up in quality, for the rather compressed shrub, fifteen to twenty feet high, wears exceedingly attractive bronze-backed, green, pointed leaves and large waxy flowers exquisite as ivory and intensely fragrant.

MAHOGANY FAMILY

TRUE MAHOGANY

Swietenia mahagoni

The True Mahogany is a *rara avis* in Hawaii, few specimens having been planted before the long row down the center of Kalakaua Avenue. These were set out about twelve years ago by the Outdoor Circle. With few exceptions the trees have thrived as their sturdy trunks, rounded full branching tops and healthy leaves attest. In time the trees should be very fine.

The "Hawaiian Mahogany" is "falsely so called" being none other than the *Acacia koa,* a fine cabinet wood in its own right.

AUSTRALIAN CEDAR

Cedrela australis

The Australian Cedar, not a Cedar, nor "Swamp Mahogany" nor "Cigar Box Tree," by all of which names it is falsely called, is one of the best timber trees of Australia. It has within a few years been planted in a hollow on the Round Top Road. It is quick-growing, pale in bark, and has long subdivided leaves. It is, however, so much less attractive than some of our native trees that a good many Islanders resent its introduction into our Forest Reserve.

Melia azedarach

"Lilac, my dear, Lilac. I must call this tree Lilac! Color, perfume,—I am back in my girlhood home in New England!" Thus the grandmother of early days to the child under the spreading Pride of India.

Nostalgia aside, this tree bearing its origin in its name, the first of many flowering trees introduced from farther tropics to Hawaii, brought beauty in its own right. Nature endowed it with fern-like foliage of large, lustrous leaves cut in elaborate lacy patterns and with multitudes of single flowers that later hold dull amber fruit, food for birds only. Mr. Rock tells us that in India the natives make necklaces of the fruit to ward off contagion.

The tree sows its own progeny. It attains distinction in height and girth. Where rains abound its rough bark attracts picturesque lichens that harmonize with its pale flowers. Its wood, handsomely marked, was long ago esteemed by the Hawaiians as material for their calabashes. The flower used with pink Mexican Creeper makes a table decoration suggestive of fine Belique or Dresden china.

MANGO FAMILY

MANGO

Mangifera indica

A tree, at once claiming the admiration of the new-comer and abounding in succulent memories for the Island-born, is the Mango.

The old time "sweet" Mango, contrasted with the "sour" from which the chutney, inevitable accompaniment of our curry, is made, did not come true from seed and so produced variations distinguished as the Mango-in-your-yard, or my-yard or his. The first Mango brought by Hawaii's ofttime benefactor Don Marin and, bearing his Hawaiian name, Manini, long outlived him. Our early Mango trees, long-lived, still hold their own among the finest shade trees of the Islands.

But many varieties have within the last twenty years been introduced and the Hawaiian stock is now greatly improved by budding, grafting or inarching. Mangoes of Honolulu are now called by special names, Alphonse, Cambodiana, Pirie, and others, certain strains being much in demand.

The Mango trunk, not too rough for climbing, may branch low or high and may attain a girth of from ten to fifteen feet and a height of eighty feet with an even greater spread of shade.

The seasons of bearing seem to be changing and the once "summer," large and "winter," small crops, to be enlarging their borders. Less gaudy than the so-called flowering trees, the springtime of the Mango, however changeable its date, calls one to drive through the city just to delight in the soft rags of burgundy silk that turn into thick, long, lanceolate, heavily-veined leaves shading from Nile- to bottle-green, and in the fragrant flowers in their bronze hues which vary from pale green to gold, copper and iron tones. Owing to climatic conditions Honolulu Mango trees are not so majestic as those of Hilo where dome upon dome of massive foliage crowns the city as the domes of a thousand mosques crown Cairo.

The fruit with its firm pulp built on a large seed of its own shape may have been the original motif of the Indian print or the Paisley shawl, the familiar design of an irregular kidney or pear. The flesh in the best varieties is free from the stringiness that marks the poor, and in color and flavor resembles the peach, particularly if used in or with ice cream. The taste is sometimes marred by a suggestion of resin or turpentine which abounds in the sap of the whole tree, even to the stem and skin of the fruit. The skin, a heavy kid-like texture, is a gay palette for nature's brush and the ripening fruit, blending scarlet, orange, rose, amber and green is the final glory of the tree. What wonder that at fruit season the Mango tree is the coveted and often the appropriated happy hunting ground of every child, and that the shirt of the descending climber is bulgy with promised satisfaction.

Wi

Spondias dulcis

"What is that tree?" exclaims the stranger when he sees the huge white-limbed Wi (pronounced after the Hawaiian fashion, vee) thrusting its rather awkward branches through the neighboring foliage of Orange, Breadfruit or Algaroba. He will be particularly curious if he sees it first in "the winter of its discontent," but perhaps it is, rather, content in this balmy climate of ours, for then it stands bereft of its long pinnate leaves, suggesting those of the Walnut, which have exchanged their green for gold and fallen with the last of the year. Freed from its own shade, in the following three months it draws the sunshine into its almost spherical fruit, size of a large plum, that follows the most unobtrusive of flowers and is grouped in clusters on short stems. Under the thin golden skin, that peels readily to the knife, lies the firm, yellow, acid flesh. The fruit holds a seed that is somewhat like a burr made of cork and extends its spines into the flesh. Though pleasant to the palate, thought by some to have a flavor suggesting pineapple, it is not at all cultivated for market and rarely appears on the table.

The Wi is known as a native of the Society Islands. The parent specimen in Hawaii stands in the center of grounds just *mauka* of the Royal Mausoleum on Nuuanu Street, formerly the home of Bishop Staley for whom the tree was planted by one of the early Hawaiian queens. It has been a large and fruitful tree for fifty years.

Pepper Tree

Schinus molle

This Brazilian tree, one of the hall-marks, so to speak, of California, has for many years had a place in Honolulu, though shorter of stature here, but because of its frailty against hard winds is less and less planted. A row of pepper trees borders a part of Keeaumoku Street. The light brown trunk with ragged bark upholds the most graceful of drooping branches and their long lacey leaves of olive green are well contrasted with the deep rose-colored "peppers" in their fringing clusters. The mother flower of the pepper, like that of many other fruit trees, is modest to inconspicuousness, a delicate loveliness of minute white blossoms that are to make way for the showy offspring.

CHRISTMAS BERRY

Schinus terebinthifolius

Another South American Schinus is much more hardy and, of rather recent importation, bids fair to run wild. It is a sturdy, shrub-like tree with dark green leaves. The upright branches of scarlet berries that follow white flowers make gay holiday wreaths and, put away without leaves, will serve two or three years.

MANGOSTEEN FAMILY

SOUR MANGOSTEEN

Garcinia xanthochymus

The Mangosteen of India and Burmah is grown somewhat scarcely as an ornamental tree. To the un-initiated it suggests by its foliage as well as its name the Mango to which it is in no way related. Unfortunately it is very unlike its cousin the Sumatran or "sweet" Mangosteen (*Garcinia mangostana*). That species has been called the queen of fruits but so far appears to have been planted in two gardens only, one on Kauai and one on Maui.

The Indian Mangosteen is one of the smaller garden trees. Its shining long, lanceolate and opposite leaves, shading from rose color when young to dark green, overlap downward making the tree cone-shaped.

The fruit appears in October and November, springing from inconspicuous white axillary flowers. When ripe it glows through the shingling leaves, in its yellow color, thin glossy skin, with size, and shape, resembling a persimmon. Although very ornamental, the fruit is of little use as its acidity is so extreme as to obliterate flavor.

KAMANI

Calophyllum inophyllum

The natives and early settlers call the imported Kamani *malihini* and the one now to be described, native. It at least long antedates the first *haole*. Bearing the same name, the two trees are unrelated botanically as their genealogies show. The Kamani, called Tamanu in Tahiti although of a different genus belongs to the Mangosteen family. It is always green, spreads little but grows very tall. Its thick and glossy leaves, oval in shape with unbroken edge and heavy veins, resemble the leaves of the India Rubber tree (*Ficus elastica*). Its flowers, in creamy clusters, are fragrant. Its comely fruit is a spherical nut nearly the size of a golf ball. Children make toy calabashes of the nuts, which take a good polish when their thin skin is removed. Though found occasionally through the city, where planted, this tree grows wild in company with the other Kamani on the round-the-island drive at the edge of the shore, for it is always a sea-lover.

MORNING GLORY FAMILY

This large family is an especial lover of the tropics. Among the many members that easily run wild in the Islands we mention but a few.

Sweet Potato —— Uala

Ipomoea Batata

Harking back to aboriginal days, the Sweet Potato vied with the Taro in feeding the Hawaiian before the first *haole* foot tracked the sea-shore. The Hawaiian name for the long-cultivated hill Round Top back of Honolulu is Ualakaa, Rolling Potato. One wonders if the ancient cultivator rolled his produce down hill to the consumer on the plain.

Pohuehue

Ipomoea maritima

On almost any shore of our islands this beach-comber may be found, laying its pale pink skirts, seamed with deep rose down its undivided corolla, upon its heavy heart-shaped leaves and basking in its own fragrance.

Moon Flower

Ipomoea bon-nox

The Hau jungles of the Tantalus region are lighted every evening by the exquisite "good-night flower" that unfolds its long white buds at dusk. Children delight in watching for the final spring when, pushed by a puff of wind, or more likely a hidden elf, the opening cup flares into the long-throated trumpet. Glistening white through the gloaming, it calls on two notes, color and perfume, to visiting moths and the dance of life ends only with dawn. A child wrote,

> "Moon flowers seem to me
> Faces of Angels.
> They watch us while we sleep."

WOODEN ROSES

Convolvulus tuberosum

"Will you buy wooden roses?" calls a child at the door. Surely here are wooden roses of thin dark brown wood lined with coffee-colored satin, the seed-vessels of the "Ceylon Morning Glory" that with palmate leaves and golden-yellow tubular flowers, wrinkled at the lips, climbs rapidly over ugly fences, a joy-giver. The "roses" make a long-lived decoration.

KUHIO VINE

Ipomoea horsfalliae

The late Prince Kuhio took much interest while Hawaiian Delegate to Washington, in sending home seeds of plants. This Ipomoea, with rich crimson, sturdy, tubular flower and dark green palmate leaf, first adorned his dwelling and there received his name. Since his death it has spread its ruddy beauty throughout the city.

MULBERRY FAMILY

MULBERRY

Morus nigra

Family ties seem elastic indeed when the Mulberry family embraces all the Figs including the Banyans and the India Rubber, not pot-bound as in Boston halls, but superb in Island gardens, and also the Breadfruit, Jak-fruit and the maker of Mulberry pies! This last arrived many decades ago. It grows from cuttings so readily and is so prolific in fruit, serving both bird and man, why should it not be in everybody's garden? Beside giving table delights it feeds the eye with its long swaying sprays of prettily cut leaves and fruit shading from rose to black flung against the sky or brought, like the fabulous Irish pig, into the parlor.

Fig

Ficus carica

Speaking of genealogy, the Fig finds mention of itself in the Book of Genesis. Perhaps the Banyan or the India Rubber members of the family, offered arboreal habitations to man long before he felt the need of leafy clothing.

Although Mr. Wilder mentions three varieties as worthy of notice in our list of Island fruits, only one kind, the Smyrna, is seen in market and, despite the difficulty that the introduced Mynah bird enjoys Figs as much as he does the army worm (the excuse for his importation) this luscious fruit should receive more general cultivation. Now that the fruit-fly has been so much reduced as a pest, the owner of a small garden will find the care of a few Fig trees slight trouble for the reward upon his table.

A mulched soil around the roots is useful. Watering should be restrained when the fruit is maturing in order to conserve richness of flavor.

The tree is low, and, like Caliban, loves to sprawl in the sun. Its leaves, rough as sand-paper, deeply lobed and irregularly palmate, hold in their axils the Figs which grow singly and practically without stem.

Children are amused, when asked to find the flower

88

of the Fig, to learn that it is inside the little pear-shaped body and, fertilized by insects, sows its fine seed as a flavor in the delicate pink pulp.

BREADFRUIT —— Ulu

Artocarpus incisa

Perhaps no tree excites the traveller new to the tropics more than that which bears "loaves of bread—the staff of life." Is his entire breakfast, Orange, Papaia, Coffee, Sugar, (Coconut) milk, and Bread (fruit) to be taken from Nature's growing hand? He looks about as if to see a golden muffin or French loaf pendent from a tree.

But the ancient Polynesian set more store by the Breadfruit than the curiosity of the visitor can match, and, in his migrations among dreamed-of islands, voyaging by the stars and his prowess in managing the canoe hollowed from mighty logs and equipped with sail of hand-woven Lauhala, he carried the difficultly-transplanted shoots of this life-giving tree, hoping for favorable climatic conditions. Long before the *haole* discovered these shores, even before the great Kamehameha united the warring islands into the kingdom of Hawaii, a group of intrepid native sailors brought the first Breadfruit, the precious Ulu, from Tahiti, a princely gift to the chiefs of Oahu. On the windward side of this island, its first home, may still be seen some of the finest specimens, for the Breadfruit craves a rain-belt as its best habitat.

Growing away from its youthful cone-shaped symmetry into more freedom of expression, but always beautiful through irregular in contour, the Breadfruit attains a height of from forty to sixty feet and gives a wide shade. Its leaf is that of a titan Oak, dark, glossy green to the eye and almost as rough as a Fig leaf to the touch. From sturdy stems on the branches spring

BREADFRUIT TREE

the minute male flowers arranged in a yellow-green catkin and the collection of female flowers which unite to form the green globes of fruit. These, spherical or slightly elongated, may grow to the size of a child's head. The fruit is covered with a heavy patterned skin, (may it not have furnished a design for *tapa* marking?) and holds, surrounding the small mother-pith, a mass of pulp which is the "bread." If the fruit is gathered, as is the Tahitian custom, not quite ripe and

BREADFRUIT

baked in the coals of a fire, then peeled snow-white from its charred covering, it is as mealy and neutral in taste as baked potato or rice. The Hawaiians prefer the well-ripened fruit which tastes a good deal like an especially sweet Sweet Potato. It is sometimes used as a *poi*, a paste made by beating the cooked fruit with water, as the *poi* from the Kalo (Taro) is made. But it is usually baked in its skin in the oven. Its stem may be pulled out just before baking, the cavity thus formed being filled with salt or sugar to increase the flavor. It is then cut or torn open, the skin preserving the heat, to be eaten with butter as a vegetable or it may be peeled or mashed like potato.

One who enjoys the luxuriant growth of this tree should see the groves of Breadfruit, self-planted and magnificent along the Hamakua coast near Hilo. The wood is durable but not used commercially, although the type canoe of the Hawaiians had its gunwale made from it. This wonderful people found uses for leaf and bark as they did of tree after tree, a lost language of utility. Aside from all its uses, even that of food, the Breadfruit for beauty alone claims a place in the garden.

BANYAN

The Banyan is conspicuous among our imported trees, appearing in several species each having marked characteristics, the large-leafed, heavy-limbed, forest-producing, from India (*Ficus benghalensis*); the Chinese (*Ficus benjamina*) smaller-leafed, with thick beard of would-be roots adorning the trunk; the *Ficus religiosa*, sacred to Hindoo and Buddhist alike, bearing delicate, birch-like leaves, more rarely planted but to be found in the Moanalua Gardens, and in India called the Peepul Tree. It seems strange to the casual observer that the Banyan is a *ficus*, but one's little daughter discovers that the fruit of the giant is a perfect "doll Fig." May a Banyan, then, have been the Fig Tree of Eden? If so, did our first parents like the Swiss Family Robinson take up residence in the much-ramified structure? Or did the Fig because of its patronage by young humanity, assume an untoward arrogance and try to thrust out all other trees, becoming by mighty strides a second Paradise?

Dr. Hillebrand brought the first Banyan to Honolulu from India, the *Ficus benghalensis*, which though doubtfully indigenous was, Mr. Rock tells us, the favorite tree of Hindoo traders and so was called by

INDIAN BANYAN TREE

their name, Banyan. Sacred to the Hindoos, it grows wild in sub-Himalayan forests, furnishing an inferior rubber, food for grazing elephants and cattle, and offering to the native fuel, linaments and anodynes for rheumatism. In time of famine the fruit, bark, leaves and shoots are all used for food.

In Honolulu none of these uses are made of the tree but since it is easily propagated by cutting the self-rooting limbs, or rather the limbs metamorphosed from hanging roots, the Banyan is a favorite where grounds are large enough to give it reasonable freedom.

The finest specimens of Chinese Banyan used to be those planted three-quarters of a century ago by Mr. A. Afong in his Chinese garden (corner of Nuuanov and School Sts.) with its tiled terrace, fountain and exotic plants. Their rapidity of growth has made them seem old trees for forty years, but now owing to the encroachments of a market building they are sadly mutilated and much hidden. Excellent specimens may be seen in Thomas Square where sometimes classes of an adjoining public school sit for lessons under their umbrageous spread.

Two fine Indian Banyans stand on Beretania St., near the corner of Punahou St. Severe tree-surgery has been administered to keep them within the bounds of necessity, but even so their branches reach over the highway.

The most notable Banyan in Honolulu was planted by the Honorable A. S. Cleghorn, father of Kaiulani, "the little Princess" at Ainahau—once, perhaps, the most alluring tropical garden in the world. In thirty years a canny Scotch hand with a gift for gardening and prompted by love of the thing planted and the one planted for, transformed a waste of sand dunes into a grove of lofty Palms festooned with Philodendron, Bignonia, Bougainvillea, neighbored by Bamboo, Breadfruit, Avocado, Saman, Tamarind, Mango, made lovely by Papyrus, Hibiscus, Lilies, Crotons and Oleander. The magnificent Banyan-king of that royal garden-grove still lives, curtailed, crowded upon, desolate, for the spirit of the gardener has followed that of her who inspired the garden and of her who was

AINAHAU SHOWING COCONUT PALMS, PHILODEN-
DRON AND CROTONS

born in its beauty. Once, deep in tree-shadows, among rocks of hoary and sacred legend, down many intersecting paths, through the grove of Coconut Palms bending over the pool of blue Water-lilies between the Banyan and the many-voiced sea, wandered splendid Peacocks, the name-bird of Likelike, Kaiulani's departed mother. Stevenson wrote shortly before he, too, left the earth:—

> "The peacocks call in vain the maid,
>   The royal maid so near a throne,
>   Her spirit fled the banyan shade;
>   They call and wait alone."

Ainahau is now a village of tiny houses, for the most part occupied by transients. In the rustle of the Palms and the falling of the nuts do the casual sojourners ever hear royal footsteps or ponder on the inevitable change and cycle of human life?

Ficus heterophylla

(often called *Ficus repens*)

One of our commonest yet most interesting creepers is known by its fruit to belong to the true Fig. It illustrates the unexpected in life, for the most delicate pattern will for a while be traced by its growth over rock-face, tree trunk or the side of a building, when suddenly the plant becomes rampant, threadlike stem turning to woody trunk, leaves trebling, quadrupling their size, the lowly head raised as if defying the sky, the sucking dove become a lion, the creeping vine, an undaunted shrub demanding to be a tree!

MYRTLE FAMILY

Eucalyptus

Few of the hundreds of varieties of Eucalyptus have found a way from the deep "bush" of Australia, where they reign as a race of giants, to these Islands, but several have been long resident with us.

The Blue Gum, *Eucalyptus globulus,* its sappy young growth of trunk, branch and leaf all deeply tinctured with blue, is full of fragrant oil and, snatched by the handful on the Tantalus Drive where in the reforestation scheme of forty years ago the Eucalyptus played an important rôle, the leaves offer a filling for a pillow to soothe and alleviate a head-cold.

The variety with the red flower is too little seen here. The visitor from Hollywood recalls its bright beauty as a roadside tree there.

The *robusta* is found in public and private grounds but the favorite in Honolulu is the *citriodora*. The characteristic scent of the Eucalyptus is, in this variety, blended with an Orange-like odor and is a delight. The tree, rapid in growth, has high aspirations and if given favorable conditions of soil, sun and water may attain twenty feet in its first year. With almost crescent gold-tipped leaves set openly on slender stems and upturned branches, it proceeds to a maturity high and wide-spread but combining delicacy with strength.

The flower of the Eucalyptus is fluffy being full of stamens and, other than the red variety, is of a creamy color.

The fruit is held in a cup something like an acorn.

While the other varieties also shed their bark, the Blue Gum trees cast their bark away in sheets and

97

stand naked like giant athletes ready for Olympic games.

Ohia Lehua

Metrosideros polymorpha

Botanists tell us that Polynesia abounds in the Ohias but that they offer perplexities as to classification: that, perhaps as much in fact as in jest, if, in the forest, one is in doubt as to a tree it may as well be called Ohia. Certainly the name *Metrosideros polymorpha* sounds wide enough to cover innumerable variations.

The visitor is more apt to meet the Ohia Lehua in the handsome dark wood floor that attracts his eye in club house or dwelling or even in railroad ties than he is in the tree. This he will find, if at all, in the mountains back of Honolulu or more likely in the woods on Hawaii on the volcano trip. The tree is almost a masquerader in its variations, the leaf differing in size and shape, being glabrous or velvety or woolly one or both sides and shifting in color from green to rose and silver. The flower may be yellow, rose or white, although scarlet is the most characteristic. It may be a shrub, as often on Oahu, gnarled and scrubby at the sea-shore, or lofty, even gigantic, producing exceedingly hard and durable lumber at elevations of several thousand feet. It is frequently a vampire, insisting on starting its life in the lap of a Tree-fern or in the arms of another tree, in after years revealing its infant nurture by its stilt-like roots that survive the decay of the foster parent they bestrode. Its scarlet blossom is one most endeared to the Hawaiian and it appears as scarlet in his passionate unwritten literature as it does in the woods where its exquisite unpetalled plumage so resembles that of the native red birds, Iiwi and Olokele, that visit it for its honey. A lei of scarlet Lehua is full of sentiment to the Hawaiian and it is celebrated in the familiar song "Sweet Lei Lehua."

MOUNTAIN APPLE —— Ohia Ai

Jambosa malaccensis

In Makiki Valley, an easy walk from the Tantalus Drive is an old and pleasing grove of the Ohia Ai, the edible Ohia. It is found of course in many other places, though perhaps less accessible, and fruit may be seen in market between July and December. Except to the thirsty tramper, these Mountain Apples have little to recommend their slight flavor. The juicy white pulp, firm almost to crispness covers a hard round seed and, shaped like a small Bellflower Apple, wears a skin that would be imperceptible save for its exquisite coloring that shades from palest pink near the short stem to deep maroon. The fruit follows a flower like that of the Ohia Lehua save that its color is crimson rather than scarlet. The leaves, a rich dark green are elliptical and six or eight inches long. They well set off the fruit and make the slender tree of from twenty-five to fifty feet in height, with branches rather short, due to the elbowing of its neighbors in the dim valley, a colorful memory.

Two or three varieties of Water Apple (other Jambosas) are cultivated in gardens though not as familiar as most trees.

99

Rose Apple

Eugenia jambos

The Eugenias and Jambosas are so close of kin in the large family of Myrtle that the Ohia Ai just described is called sometimes by one name, sometimes by the other.

The Rose Apple, a West Indian, while the Jambosas are Malayan, if given room in the garden, is, with its pale grey bark, its graceful spread of ascending branches, its dark, pointed slender-oval leaves, and height of thirty or more feet, a comely tree all its evergreen year. In the spring among the leaves which are then rosy and silky, appear pompons of cream-colored flowers (a mass of stamens and pistils) gladdening the eye and attracting the bees. They are replaced during the summer by still more attractive fruit the size of Christmas apples, slightly elongated in shape and keeping the green flower calyx (a little memory of youth) as an adornment to set off the rosy cheek of the creamy thin-skinned globes. "What is it like?" asks the stranger, and as he crunches through the compact sweet pulp that like a shell holds in its hollow a single dry brown spherical seed, he exclaims "You're right, it does taste as a rose smells!"

Spanish Cherry

Eugenia brasiliensis

A much smaller tree, hardly more than a shrub, this Eugenia, hailing from Brazil and called Brazilian Plum, more commonly Spanish Cherry, was one of the chosen plants brought by the honored Don Marin. Its trunk may retain branches close to the ground. Its

PINK AND WHITE SHOWER (Cassia nodosa)

leaves are heavier, blunter, and more compactly arranged than those of the Rose Apple. Its flowers and fruit are smaller, the latter a cherry in shape and size, its persistent calyx terminating a purple skin that dries to a kid-like texture. The pulp, soft, succulent and delicious in flavor, holds a single round, pale green seed. The tree fruits in midsummer although like many another tropic plant it is not meticulous as to season.

French Cherry

Eugenia uniflora

This native of Brazil has borne its nickname French Cherry for some sixty years in Honolulu. It is a shrub with small dainty pointed leaves and it recalls a New England spring when, as if covered with white powder, it bursts into small fluffy flowers resembling Hawthorn bloom. The flower soon makes way for the fruit that in a soft pulp holds one (perhaps divided) pale seed. Deeply grooved, with its bright transparent skin and retained minute calyx, the cherry is as ornamental as a fairy lantern. Indeed the bush becomes a veritable Christmas Tree when the fruit, in all stages of ripening at once, adorns it in many colors from green through yellow, orange, vermilion, cardinal to maroon. Only the last color bids the taste of the knowing, for the acidity of the earlier stages, excellent for the jelly-pot supersedes the spice and sweetness of full maturity.

Java Plum

Syzigium jambolana

The Java Plum, a native of Southern Asia, is one of the commonest trees in Honolulu. Two varieties, differing slightly to the casual eye in size of tree, leaf and fruit, have long been resident. The smaller variety, imported by Dr. Hillebrand, is much the more common and develops so rapidly from self-planted seeds as sometimes to become a nuisance. In its seedling days it is hardly to be distinguished from the Rose Apple and, having supposedly planted the latter, one is sometimes unhappily the possessor of the former. It is however often chosen as a break-wind. Growing to a height of thirty or forty feet with a whitish bark and abundant dark leathery pointed leaves set on gracefully drooping branches, it makes a stately shade tree. The fragrant white blossoms of summer give place to purple-black fruit and during October and November the ground is strewn with brittle twigs and stained by the fruit. The fruit, the size and shape of a Filbert nut, is puckery to the tongue and too sugar-consuming to be much used for jam, but it is incessantly sought by noisy Mynahs and, out of school hours, by swarming children.

GUAVA

Psidium guayava pomiferum

Among the throng of trees and shrubs, indigenous and imported, the Guava, kamaaina and ubiquitous, appears like a rustic beauty in short full skirts. Clad in faun-colored, mottled bark and shapely oval leaves, rough-textured but prettily veined, with dainty, round, white and fragrant flowers, resembling those of a plum, tucked closely in their axils, and with abundant golden fruit, round to oval, scenting the air and strewing the ground, Guava lives the fruitful, healthy life we associate with happy peasantry.

Driving across the Wahiawa plains or up Tantalus, or in the less cultivated parts of our valleys, one meets this cheerful food-producer, Many who have known the Guava only in the dark, stiff, tinned jelly imported from some other tropical countries have missed the delights of the fresh fruit, its pink pulp sliced, chilled and eaten raw with cream and sugar, or delicately boiled whole with syrupy juice, or made into

GUAVA

whip, sherbet, ice cream, marmalade, or quivering jellies from pale amber to crimson according to quantity and length of cooking. Several times a year the discriminating housewife gathers the common sour variety for cooking and the, also wild, sweet Guava, its flesh a deep old-rose, for uncooked use.

Honolulu gardens sometimes cultivate the Lemon Guava, shaped like the lemon and lighter in color outside and in than the wild varieties, also the early imported but rare Waiawi (pronounced vy-ah-vee) a tall handsome tree with small dark leathery leaves and a small pointed yellow fruit, except in color resembling the Strawberry Guava. This last, a later importation, is an attractive garden shrub with round fruit the color of a very ripe strawberry and having a decided flavor of that fruit. It makes a fine jelly though too scarce for commercial use.

Guava lovers eat skin and all, for no one can or need chew or eschew the hard seeds so many and so imbedded in the luscious acid pulp, and the skin has a flavor all its own.

POMEGRANATE

Punica granatum

The Pomegranate is found in Hawaii in several varieties and, being one of the early importations, graces many old gardens. A native of Southwestern Asia, it has climbed several thousand feet up the Himalayas. Native also in Northern Africa, whence, receiving its name from Carthage, it was introduced into Europe, it doubtless adorned the tables of Dido and Cleopatra. The tree, or shrub, is dainty in character, dressed in small, shiny, red-veined leaves poised on ruby-colored petioles. Its thorns are observable but not bothersome. When hung with vermilion, bell-shaped flowers and pendent, bright, globes of fruit, it recalls the embroidered temple vestments described in Deuteronomy. The fruit, about the size of an apple, retains the flower calyx which it wears as a crown. Its covering is heavy to leatheriness and is pale gold with flushed cheeks, our climate seeming to withhold the deep red color that characterizes the Pomegranates so abundantly displayed in the stalls of Italy. When fully ripe the fruit bursts its casing and reveals its inner self, Uncounted small seeds are each inclosed in a crystal-clear ruddy pulp so delicate as to seem an unfermented wine gushing into the mouth as one bites into the fruit. It is difficult to manage as the seed-holding pulp lies in many sections of a yellow, kid-like texture which does not enhance the taste. Indeed, eating a Pomegranate seems like eating an idea rather than a food.

OLIVE FAMILY

Olive

Olea europea

The true Olive of the old world is here in a world still in the making, but, as if homesick, it rarely brings forth the little black fruit that is as familiar in California as in Southern France or Italy. In spite of its appealing beauty it is too little cultivated here. A notable planting has, however, been made at "La Pietra" the Italian Villa on the slope of Diamond Head. There, consorted with the Cypress, also unfamiliar in Honolulu, under sunny walls holding ancient statues and urns, the Olives look upon as blue a sea as any their ancestors knew. Standing on a little hill they turn the mind to another green hill far away where old gnarled trees hold deep associations in their rugged breasts. Since the Olive is long-lived and easily propagated from cuttings, layers and suckers, one would suggest that these lovely trees so full of tranquil, silver grace be planted in gardens for meditation about the homes and churches of Honolulu.

STAR JASMINE

Jasminum multiflorum (or *grandiflorum*)

This favorite climber, luxuriant in pointed leaves and ever-blooming clusters of seven-to-nine pointed snowy stars, attests its membership in the family by its Olive-like black fruit. It should have a place in every moonlit garden.

Pikaki

Jasminum pubescens

The most beloved of leis, not forgetting those of the poetic Maile, the queenly Kolona, the royal Ilima, and the sacred Plumieria, is the dainty white circlet of fragrant Pikaki. The Princess Likelike chose, as did the goddess Juno, the Peacock as her symbol, and from association the royal mistress and her favorite flower acquired the name of the bird. Since the death of the Princess, so the Hawaiians say, the Pikaki, single or double, a fragile flower nestled against downy-backed leaves and turning blue at the lips when it dies, is hard to grow; hence the lei is rare.

ORANGE FAMILY

Perhaps the first of this prized family to arrive at these islands was the Orange (*Citrus aurantium sinense*) brought, as were so many other gifts, by Vancouver about the beginning of the nineteenth century. From one island to another the seed has been carried, producing trees that come true and give delicious fruit. The color of oranges in Hawaii, even those descended from so colorful a variety as the Navel, changes to yellow, often a greenish yellow even when ripe and often is russet. Thickness of skin varies but is usually rather thick and the seeds are numerous. The fruit is uniformly full of juice of a fine rich flavor, the pulp being exceedingly delicate.

For years the Kona Orange (taking its name from the district of its best production) has been marketed but it is a pity that more attention is not given to the cultivation of this excellent fruit in home gardens. True, it is subject to blight and sometimes needs spraying, but now the arch enemy the fruit fly is so largely under control, gardeners should rise above other discouragements. Like all other fruit trees the Orange needs to have its dead wood and its inner growth pruned away to admit free circulation of air. Fertilization and careful watering bring their reward.

The hardy Pomelo or Chinese Shadduck (*Citrus decumana*) round or pear-shaped, much larger than the Orange but having the family characteristic look and fragrance of flower, leaf and fruit, deserves more planting. It is rather dry in pulp but makes an excellent salad or fruit cocktail alone or combined with Avocado or Papaia. The Grape Fruit, a variety of the *Citrus decumana,* imported from Florida has done well in some gardens. More rare are the Lime, Lemon, and Japanese, or Glove-skin, Orange.

The Chinese Orange or *Citrus japonica* which Gerritt Wilder tells us is the *Hazara* (signifying thousand of fruit) is an old resident and, once common, is since the coming of the fruit fly little seen. The tree in bearing is most ornamental and its fruit, really orange colored and twice the size of a cherry furnishes an abundant juice that makes a good substitute for the more difficultly cultivated Lemon. This Orange combined with Papaia makes a uniquely delicious marmalade. Cultivation should be resumed.

MOCK ORANGE

Murraya exotica

A true member of the Orange family in spite of the denial in its name, this shrub, growing from ten to twenty feet in height, is well adapted for hedges but is rarely planted as such. Singly or in groups it is always satisfying in size, symmetry and beauty of foliage (its glossy leaves made up of from three to seven leaflets shading from apple- to bottle-green) but is most delightful when powdered with its exquisite white flowers that breathe forth a fragrance like that of its Citrus cousins. Its red fruit, about the size of a Coffee berry is equally red and pretty. Long a favorite, the Mock Orange is more and more planted as a garden treasure.

PALMS

Loulu

Pritchardia

To describe the Palms now living in Honolulu would be to fill a book. Only a few will be mentioned in this modest guide, but they must include the Loulu, for it thrills the blood of the mountain climber to come upon a specimen of the single genus indigenous in Hawaii. It is the genus Pritchardia, called by the Hawaiians Loulu, and, found also elsewhere in the islands of the Pacific, almost all of its species are native

WINE PALM

109

here. Of these ten, four (one on each of the larger islands), have been found within the last twenty years. Possibly other species are awaiting you, or you, as discoverer!

Mr. Rock describes the genus as "Tall trees with terminal, fan-shaped palmatisect leaves and unarmed petioles."

Loulu palms are not easily obtainable but some of them are grown for *lanai* plants and then set into the ground by appreciative *kamaainas*.

Although a Loulu hat made from young leaves is excellent, its making involves, through carelessness or indolence, havoc and destruction of these cherished Palms.

COCONUT PALM —— Niu

Cocos nucifera

Indigenous? One loves to believe that this tree, known throughout Polynesia as Niu (with local modifications of the name) was the far precursor of man when, in giant double canoes splendidly wrought from the boles of southern trees and winged with mat-sails woven by patient toil in exquisite designs, he swept up across Oceanica in hopeful, courageous ignorance, guided by the stars, swayed by the currents and in the mists of fifteen centuries ago disembarked on the lava shores of Hawaii. In how many an earlier century the nuts of the Coconut Palm, flung upon the bosom of southern waters floated, now long becalmed, now tempest-driven, to their happy destiny, there is no knowing but long-blessed has been the coral beach or the lava shore that offered the wave-tossed tree-germs in their stout shells an abiding place.

The constant winds of these favored Islands prevent the Coconut Palm from attaining such luxuriant foliage as is to be found in Pacific Islands farther south or in Jamaica. In spite of still greater hindrance from an enemy moth it grows slowly to a height of a hundred feet, though a Samoan variety planted of late years offers its crown of leaves and fruit at a man's height. Curiously enough the direction of the prevailing wind not always accounts for the marked inclination of the trunk seaward. It were as if remembering the faithful nurse that brought it hither and nourished it from infancy to old age by waves high enough to water but not to displace the once established tree. It were as if willing to give its offspring to be carried to yet other shores.

Although Hawaii has not developed a copra industry, a grove of Coconut Palms is a good investment and a good inheritance for the tree produces freely and the retail price is good. Owners of property along the shore are therefore thrifty as well as appreciative of distinctive beauty in replacing old groves in which tree after tree centuries old is at last decapitated by time and, a weird menace of death, falls or is cut down. A few public spirited citizens have planted groves. One such is at Fort Kamehameha, another at Fort Armstrong. Some enthusiasts advocate the planting of one Coconut Palm by each householder each year.

The finest grove in Honolulu is that of The Old Plantation where ten thousand trees make one of the most picturesque features of the city. Another grove at Lahaina, a former capital of the group, is famous as the planting of Queen Kapiolani who quickly seized

111

the altruistic idea, presented her by the missionaries, of planting something for future generations to enjoy.

An old Coconut Palm is distinguished from other Palms by its superlative height, inclined position and rough, light brown trunk. The leaves of its crown are golden-green, heavier and longer than those of the Royal Palm, fewer, larger and more sweeping than those of the Date Palm.

As to the productivity of the Coconut Palm, how many nuts on such beautiful clusters as adorn the corridors of the Royal Hawaiian Hotel, would, unplucked, grow from the deep yellow blossom stems into huge triangular husks, is a matter dependent upon various conditions, variety of nut, kind of soil, water supply, etc. To one familiar with the water and meat of the young nut, the prepared article of commerce is "desecrated" as well as desiccated, while to one knowing only the hard nut, the "spoon-food" and drink of the immature nut is insipid.

The life-bud of the tree eaten in the South Seas in time of famine has remarkable richness and delicacy as a salad food, but, naturally, is obtainable only when for some reason a tree must be felled. Among innumerable uses of the tree products are scrubbing brushes and door mats made from the husk, pergola supports from sections of felled trees, screens, mats and hats made from leaves. May not the brown "cloth" in the axils of the leaves and used for the lining of hanging baskets have been the first suggestion to primitive man of cloth-weaving?

Perhaps no one has better described the Coconut Palm than Whittier, the New England poet, as far removed from the land of the Palm as its fabled lover the Northern Pine.

ROYAL PALM

Oreodoxa regia

By what happy and nearly-missed incidents are many great satisfactions in life reaped!

In 1849 two young native princes with Dr. G. P. Judd as Minister Plenipotentiary were sent on a

ROYAL PALMS

special embassy to Europe by the Royal Hawaiian Government. Some weeks after the return of Dr. Judd, his wife, it is said, discovered in his pocket forgotten seeds of the Royal Palm, gathered during his travels. These seeds produced the parent Royal Palms in Honolulu, a stately pair one either side the gate on the premises of Mr. S. D. Baldwin, corner of Nuuanu Avenue and Bates Street.

Honolulu has many fine specimens among the off-spring of these trees. Farther toward the mountains on this same Nuuanu Avenue and near Wyllie Street stand, in private grounds, two notable avenues (one straight and one curved) of Royal Palms resembling well-matched monoliths of grey granite.

Independent of wind or shade in its absolutely vertical growth, this palm is most dependent for its symmetry on a steady water-supply, lacking which, instead of towering in a perfect column, it will bulge and shrink alternately in sad distortions.

The Royal Palm has noble proportions, a columnar form, a striking succession of dark rings marking the leaf-scar on its pale grey surface, and finally a crown of superbly-arching, glistening, green leaves, among which, in succession, appear clusters of corn-colored blossoms, springing from silky, white-lined, canoe-shaped bracts. Bees hover over the honey-holding blossoms, but the value of the fruit seems to be only for birds and the reproduction of its own statuesque self.

DATE PALM

Phoenix dactylifera

In Arabia of the old world, and Arizona of the new, the Date Palm has a worth in metal as yellow as its fruit, and a single tree is an enviable inheritance, yielding revenue for hundreds of years.

Since this palm is bisexual and naturally the seeds do not "come true" the only sure way of propagating fertile trees is by planting suckers from the mother plant. The art of doing this has not been learned in Honolulu, consequently, while Date Palms abound,

DATE PALM

115

many are sterile and there is not even a local market supply of the fruit.

Unlike the Royal and Coconut Palms the Date does not shed its leaves and if left to nature's way, would present a shaggy, shingled appearance. As, however, the Date is planted for ornament, its leaves are cut tidily one by one, and the trunk presents a peculiarly rugged surface. In the leaf-crevices seeds and fern-spores often lodge and grow, increasing the luxuriant tropic effect.

The pinnate leaf of the common variety is sharp-pointed, stiff, upward slanting, and bluish-green in color, while that of another variety is longer, gracefully pendent, and olive-green tipped with bronze.

A solitary Palm in symmetry of shape, lofty height, and rich color, especially when the flame-colored blossoms and clusters of dates spring rocket-like among the steel lances of its leaves, is a sight to hold the eye, and such an avenue as may be seen in the grounds of the Queen's Hospital, is a picture long to be cherished.

Wine, or Ragged-Leaf Palm

Caryota urens

This Palm was much planted forty or fifty years ago but seems to be dying out of Honolulu. Perhaps it is a case of out of sight out of mind for although the tree attains a height of fifty feet the span of its life is barely a score of years. This is a pity for the tree is rapid of growth and the irregularly cut leaflets make the Palm a desirable house or *lanai* plant for several years and in its later life the huge tassels of fruit are beautiful in the mass, in single lei-like strings and in the separate blossoms or berries. The spadices succeed each other downward from the crest of the tree until its death. In India the sap of the young spadix is boiled and made into sweet or fermented wine.

PANDANUS FAMILY

Screw Pine —— Hala

Pandanus odoratissimus

If the Coconut Palm is the first love among the trees of primitive man the Hala must be its rival for the necessities and comforts of life it supplies. The Hawaiians call the tree Hala or Puhala (from the head-like bunches of fruit) or Lauhala (from the leaf) designating the most useful part. The name Screw Pine describes the tortuous thread of upward growth of the large whorls of spiny-edged, linear leaves. Not a Palm, it resembles one in the fibrous character of trunk, leaf and fruit-covering. Like the Coconut Palm it is a coast-dweller although found also inland and sometimes in mountainous districts. It grows to a height of twenty feet, is many branched, never large of girth, but always weird, sometimes uncanny, in appearance, a gargoyle of trees, clutching the rocks with stiff, brown roots (grotesque skeleton fingers) that reach down from the trunk a long distance for support and sustenance.

Each year its small compound flowers appear masquerading in large showy white bracts (the related *Ie Ie, Freycinetia arnotti,* affecting scarlet) that perch on the branches like Birds of Paradise, tails waving in the breeze. The matured fruit is an orange-colored globe, like a galaxy of little lights, each nut covered with a long-pointed husk, the big end out and having a glossy surface. These nuts are fondly strung by the

HALA TREES

Hawaiians into long leis although they are as heavy in odor as in weight. The nuts are also chewed for pastime by the idle or ruminative.

HALA FLOWER

HALA FRUIT

The value of this unique tree is not that of shade, fuel or food. It is cherished as a fabric producer. The common variety in Hawaii is used for hats, fans, baskets, portfolios, etc., but especially for floor mats, pleasing, durable and used by native and foreigner alike. No inconsiderable task and skill are involved in preparing the stiff, thorny, dried leaves for weaving material but hala-craft is still preserved among the country folk and is also taught in schools.

PASSION-FLOWER FAMILY

GRENADILLA

Passiflora quadrangularis

This remarkable member of a tropical American family that has several representatives in Hawaii is so little planted as to be a stranger to many a *kamaaina*. Having a large edition of that strange flower so satisfying to the Christian mystic in its symbolism of purple, red or white colors and in forms suggesting the Trinity, crown, cross, thorns and flails, it has also an enlarged growth throughout stem, leaf, tendril and fruit. The fruit is like a swollen cucumber, a pale yellow-green in color and from five to nine inches in length. Its pulp is succulent and delicious and may be eaten as it is or made into sherbet.

PURPLE WATER LEMON —— Lilikoi

Passiflora edulis

The fruit of this vigorous and comely vine is not marketed but grows wild in the mountains. We have from our saddles gathered the hard-shelled, egg-sized purple fruit from tree boughs in the mountains of Kauai at an elevation of three thousand feet, but it also flourishes in the hills back of Honolulu. Its leaves are three-lobed with handsome toothed edges. The flowers are white tinged with purple. The inside of the fruit is an intricate composition of color. Like that of the Guava, the pulp, which is agreeably acid, must be swallowed seeds and all!

Yellow Water Lemon

Passiflora laurifolia

This is one of the oddest fruits in market and is obtainable in winter. As large as a turkey's egg but nearer spherical in shape, its yellow skin will chip off as an egg shell will, uncovering a thick white skin that holds the sweet, soft pulp. This, like the content of the egg, may be sucked through a hole in the skin and it may be swallowed with impunity, seeds and all! Like other members of its family, this vine has admirable foliage. The leaf is oval ending in a sharp point (something like the Milo). The flower is white. The vine runs wild in the woods.

Papaia

Carica Papaia

Of late years the Papaia, which fifty years ago was little used save as chicken feed or as a substitute for pumpkin in pies or puddings, is ubiquitous upon the Honolulu breakfast table. Since the tree though short-lived is quick of growth and pleasing to the eye, one wonders why it is not planted against every householder's dining room or *lanai*. As one looks into the half of this melon-like orange-gold fruit lying on his plate and realizes that any of those velvety black seeds (with a pleasant peppery taste of their own), if planted while fresh might in a year give him back a fruit as luscious as that he is eating, he feels as if at Aladdin's table. But truth sometimes out-magics fairy lore. The roots are voracious for rich food and the imbricated leaves, sometimes two feet across their soft outreaching palms, seek moisture and air not primarily for trunk and stem which are pithy and hollow nor for the exquisite waxy-white flowers but for the nourishment of the crowning fruit. Dividing honors and tasks, the Papaia is usually dioecious and the knowing see to it that their groves of fertile trees contain some male trees. They are distinguished in appearance thus. The flower of the female tree is larger and borne close to the trunk while the small flower of the male hangs in clusters on long pendent stems. The latter flower is a favorite for the daintiest of leis. Occasionally a male tree produces fruit, and excellent fruit, for nature is untrammelled in her ways.

There is much variation in the fruit in quality and size. A Papaia may weigh from one to eight pounds. Both dwarf and tall trees are grown. Though usually branchless, the tree may branch. When it dwindles toward the top, the fruit grows inferior and the tree should give place to a fresh planting. Without season, the fruit is to be had all the year round. It is used in many ways, diced with other fruit and chilled for a fruit-cup, used with or without combination as a salad, baked for a short while with sugar and lemon as a sweet vegetable, made into puddings or pies or sherbet or ice cream.

PAPAIA TREE

Children might enjoy planting their own Papaia trees not only for the fruit but for "playing lady" parasols, leaf-stem whistles, hollowed-branch canoes, or green-fruit Jack o'lanterns.

Because of the pepsin which permeates the tree, some people chew the seeds as a remedy for indigestion, others wrap tough meat in the leaves for a short time, put a piece of the fruit into the corners of the roast pan, or hang a fowl in the Papaia tree, as a means of insuring tenderness of fibre.

PICKEREL-WEED FAMILY

Water Hyacinth

Erichhornia crassipes

Not to mention the Waterlilies familiar in northern climates nor the Lotus introduced and used by our Oriental residents, we call attention to a stately weed that, like many a pleasure, if run to excess becomes a curse. Kept afloat by globular air vessels made by enlarged portions of the stems just below the heart-shaped fleshy leaves, and trailing roots as ethereal as fine seaweed, this plant in season lifts erect racemes of shaded lavender flowers resembling Hyacinths but larger and more delicate in texture. A single plant in a deep glass vessel of water is interesting and decorative in the house. A small pool crowded with these wind-and-current-moved isles of beauty is much worth while, but, untended and uncurbed, the Water Hyacinth chokes streams and rivers and if allowed to start in waterways, is often a very costly indulgence.

PINE FAMILY

KAURI PINE

Agathis australis

In visiting New Zealand it is a matter of regret if one is unable to visit the Kauri forests. Mr. Rock avers that specimens exist there twenty-four feet in diameter and four thousand years old. The few specimens here, in private gardens or in the grounds of the Board of Agriculture, are pigmies to those just mentioned, still are forty feet high. They prove themselves to be Pine trees without Pine needles, having broad leathery leaves that are pale green to rosy when young. The tree abounds in resin. This flows from wounds like turpentine but congeals into an amber-like gum, much prized in New Zealand and used in ornamental ways.

The tree seems to grow slowly in Honolulu. One in our garden, planted four years ago, is only five feet high while a neighboring Eucalyptus, planted the same day, towers twenty feet above it. It has just now produced, encircling the central tree-bud, which in its formal arrangement of leaves resembles the Pineapple, five seeming flowers like Tuberoses of old ivory with the rosy petals curved back. But day by day they are revealing themselves to be not flowers at all but young branches blushing as they draw out distances between their petal-like leaves. Soon they will take on the color and toughness of fibre that belong to the mature growth. There is evidence, also, that slow to start this tree gathers an acceleration of speed in growth.

NORFOLK ISLAND PINE

Araucaria excelsa

Again returning thanks to the Antipodes, we call attention to the Norfolk Island Pine, or rather we let it from its height of one hundred and fifty feet call our attention. As Mrs. Charles Hubbard, a gardener beloved of Hawaii, says, "this tree is an exclamation point and should be planted only where exclamation is warranted!" A good example of such planting is seen on Nuuanu Avenue where the raised "index finger" points to the triangular blue mountain on the way to the Pali.

. These lofty trees, brought here nearly a century ago when imported trees were few, and, outliving their planters, mark the gardens of many plantation managers throughout the islands.

Arranged usually in pairs in Honolulu, elsewhere, as on the heights above Sydney Harbor, they produce a fine effect in groups and groves. Perhaps we have not room enough in our "right little, tight little island" for such arrangement.

Stiff, evergreen branches, with leaves turned up, suggesting Pine trees of Northern lands and yet in every way different, in some varieties grow in an irregular ascension, in others, lie in horizontal whorls, layer after layer up the tapering shaft like the branches of an artificial Christmas tree. Indeed, certain old families in Honolulu kept in the cellar a German "tree," into the ascending holes of which, Norfolk Island Pine branches were placed at Christmas time.

The nostalgic name, Norfolk Island Pine, recalls its limited native abode but this is only one of four Araucarias to be found in Honolulu, the others being

A. Cunninghamii, A. Cookii (named for Captain Cook) and *A. Bidwillii.* This last is the Bunya-Bunya of Queensland and is rarer here than the others. Examples of it with its rough, curling bark and exceedingly dark, shiny, sharp-pointed leaves and whorled branches, stand in grounds *mauka* and *waikiki* of School Street and *makai* and *ewa* of the same street.

This family may be grown from cuttings.

PLUMIERIA FAMILY

The Frenchman Charles Plumier has the distinction of being remembered by a flower family having thirteen hundred species grouped in thirty-two genera. One genus, also, bears his name. Of the Plumierias the yellow species has long been resident and in later years a few, shading from rose to dark cerise, have been introduced by Gerritt Wilder and others and have been hybridized by crosses between the *Plumieria acutifolia* and the *Plumieria rubra.*

Plumieria acutifolia

This flower with us is known as Plumieria but in the Far East is more commonly known as Frangipani or the Temple Flower. There seems but a short step between its constant use in the temples of Asia and its planting in abundance in the cemeteries of Honolulu. But this sacred or semi-sacred use does not prevent its being used, as it is conspicuously, as a greeting of friendliness, the leis given to arriving or departing guests on our busy docks being so often and agreeably made of this unique flower.

127

Crisp and compact, one petal folding part way round the next, delicately tinted inside and out, the flower has delicious fragrance and an endurance against wilting greater than many of our tropic flowers. Flower, leaf and stem are all abundantly provided with a milky sap which is found in other genera of this family. The

PLUMIERIA

tree may grow as high as twenty feet but is often smaller. As its leaves, some twelve inches long, are handsomely pointed and veined, the tree with its clusters of exquisite flowers would be beautiful but for the fact that the branching is awkward and the tree is destitute of leaves many months including the period of bloom. Some people plant evergreen shrubs like Hibiscus in the same clump so as to spare the sight of the pale and ungainly limbs. Although the Plumieria bears seed in long follicles, it is usually propagated by cuttings. *Plumieria alba* (white) is smaller flowered, less common, and keeps its leaves.

GIANT ALLAMANDA

Allamanda hendersonii

The Allamanda, a resident for more than half a century, is practically perennial, bursting forth into exultant yellow bloom now and again when freshened by

GIANT ALLAMANDA

rains or in response to pruning or especial fertilization. There are few varieties of Allamanda in Honolulu. The *hendersonii* is the one commonly seen and called

129

Giant, and the *carthartica* is a small shrub bearing a much smaller and stiffer flower. In Brazil there are as many as a dozen different varieties. The *hendersonii*, found in eastern greenhouses was brought to England from British Guiana, and thence to the United States about 1865.

Like many other plants having a milky sap, the Allamanda wilts quickly on cutting and can be used indoors only by keeping the stems immersed for about half an hour in water almost at boiling temperature. Cuttings for planting will however, like cuttings of Oleander, root easily if kept in cold water a fortnight.

With its whorls of glossy leaves and its abundance of yellow blossoms displayed throughout the year, the Allamanda is a familiar adornment on arbor and house-trellis or on the ground as a sidewalk border. It grows rapidly, is very clean and is long-lived, offering its pretty, fragrant, flower-cups as playthings to successive generations of children.

CARISSA

Carissa caranda

Carissa, tracing her first name back to the ancient Sanskrit, her second, to the Marathi of India, is a maiden-like shrub of much attractiveness. She suggests, however, a character long ago described as "sweet but thorny." Small dark leaves set opposite on thorny branches are a good background for fragrant white star flowers and their following red, edible drupes. A little yard on the Round Top Road has adopted a fashion of India in using this pretty thorn as a fence to protect an exposed vegetable garden.

CROWN FLOWER —— Kolona

Calotropis gigantea

A few years ago this plant, the Indian Giant Milkweed, was hardly known outside the grounds of the late Queen Liliuokalani. After her death it became widely disseminated and now one of the most common as well as the most admired of leis is made of this flower. The plant grows readily from slip into a large shrub with long single branches or a small tree, its foliage being a white green and the large almost-round heavily veined leaves having a white fuzz beneath. The leaves, alas, are ravaged by the striped caterpillars that must precede the dark jade-like cocoons and the happy golden-brown butterflies. In unguarded places the shrubs may also be badly broken by children preying upon them for the lei-making flowers. The flowers are of amethyst colors with edges suggesting rose-quartz and are so remarkable in modelling as to resemble carved beads of those stones. The plant is full of milky sap and it is difficult to keep from wilting branches cut for the house.

Beaumontia grandiflora

Many arbors in Honolulu are the proud support of this exceedingly beautiful growth that in February piles, like rosy snow, on its dark, long and heavy green leaves, clusters of cup-shaped flowers suggesting the Eucharist Lily. It is native in northern India.

Stephanotis floribunda

Sometimes called Kaiulani's flower, this lovesome vine was brought to Honolulu about the time the "Little Princess" was born. The sturdy vine bears heavy dark waxy leaves upon which at different seasons of the year rest clusters of waxy white flowers, which are tubes ending in stars and filled with an appealing fragrance.

Wax Plant

Hoya carnosa

With leaves resembling those of the Stephanotis this Wax Plant in varieties, some, plush-like with scarlet central dots, some, cream-white small stars in compact clusters, pours forth a seductive fragrance at night.

Oleander

Nerium indica

Our Oleander is first cousin to the Nerium oleander of classic Greece but unlike that ancient flower has a delicious fragrance. It has developed many varieties in its species and runs a long gamut of color,—dark red, cerise, bright pink, pale pink, salmon, buff, white; and the flowers are either single or double. Like other members of the Plumieria family it has a thick white milky sap. This is poisonous.

Usually a shrub, some varieties, especially the double cerise, rise to a height of twenty or more feet, being woody and thick at the base although branching from the ground.

The leaves, long and pointed, stiff and brittle and of a dark green color make the Oleander a fine foliage plant in its own right and offer an excellent background for its clusters of flowers of whatever shade. One variety with insignificant blossoms has variegated leaves of yellow and green.

The Oleander is almost perennial in bloom but spring is its heyday and since the flowers are borne on the new growth, the wise gardener prunes his cuttings from the old wood during periods of rest and waters and fertilizes especially after the new shoots start.

The fruit is an ornamental seed-pod but is disregarded for reproduction since cuttings are more satisfactory.

In Italy the Oleander is planted in tubs as often as in the ground. In Bermuda Oleander hedges are famous but they are little favored among the Hibiscus hedges of Honolulu. In Los Angeles the Oleander may be seen as a sidewalk tree and it has so been planted in Honolulu between the Coconut Palms along Kalakaua Avenue.

Since odor is the chief key to association, the scent of Oleander opens many mansions of memory throughout the world.

BE-STILL TREE

Thevetia neriifolia

This is a small but pretty tree sure to attract a stranger's eye because of its multitude of shiny, quivering, narrow, green leaves and its golden tubular flowers with ruffled edges that suggest a flock of canaries perched all over the slender branches. Although it is sometimes called Yellow Oleander and was named *neriifolia* because of the resemblance its leaves bear to those of the Nerium, it is only a distant cousin, —one of a thousand kin. In Ceylon the seeds are called lucky beans and are worn as charms.

Vinca

Also of this family is the sprawling *Vinca,* embracing the *rosea* that seeks companionship of color near the magenta Bougainvillea, the *rosea alba,* pure white that claims a place in any garden of night, and *oculata rubra,* white with a red rimmed pigeon-eye center. In Kona varieties of *Vinca* have turned into wild flowers.

MAILE

MAILE

Alyxia olivaeformis

Last but not least to be mentioned is our native Maile. With fragrant glossy leaves and tiny black olive-like fruit it climbs the trees of the higher forests. It offers welcome and grace to the *malihini,* breathes poetry and loved association to the *kamaaina,* decks the festal board, is worn in leis by the new arrival, the departing friend, the especially favored, and covers the biers or entwines the urns of our dead.

POTATO FAMILY

This family like the Smith family of humans contains a large variety of members.

Does the juicy Tomato (*Lycopersicum esculentum*) blush over cousinship with the dusky miner, Potato?

Does the Potato (*Solanum tuberosum*) jump out of the ground to declare his importance in Hawaiian commerce, when before Sugar was king and Pineapple was queen, he was exported to the younger civilization in California, and as a return courtesy California children were sent to Honolulu schools?

Does the Mexican Cup of Gold (*Solandra grandiflora*) dimpled bud bursting forth in trumpet shape, look, from its glory of color, luxuriance of foliage and height attained by sturdy climbing, with concealed envy at lowly cousin Poha (Cape Gooseberry, *Physalis peruviana*) among her velvet leaves, hiding her yellow-berry-head in her green-calyx poke-bonnet while waiting an invitation to make the best jam in the world?

Does the slender Floribundio (*Datura arborea*) bowed by her heavy, long, white flowers remember ringing her Wedding Bells in a knell and blowing her Angel Trumpets when the little child, whose marble effigy in the Nuuanu Cemetery has been a warning for sixty years, made food of her wonderful bloom? And does she acknowledge as close kin the troublesome weed Kikania (*Datura stramonium*)?

Did the little shrub of our grandmothers' gardens (the *Brunsfelsia latifolia* from South America) gather her purple-fading-to-white flowered skirts and make a dainty curtsey to welcome the later comers, the Potato Vines, *Solanum wendlandii* with large clusters of lavender flowers, and its smaller-flowered sisters, blue,

CUP OF GOLD

and white, and also the handsome Potato Tree (*Solanum macranthum*—planted in Nursery grounds Makiki Street) with its purple-blue and white flowers bunched against irregularly but attractively sculptured leaves? Violet-breathed, modest, gracious with her frequent blooming, undoubtedly she did!

Does the gentle Queen of the Night (*Cestrum nocturnum*) object to being called Chinese Ink-berry?

Chinese visitors like better our name Chinese Jasmine. They, in China, call her "Gold-and-Silver." Keeping watch by night, moonlight-colored in her frequent flowers (tiny pale green tubes with starry tips), resting

FLORIBUNDIO

between blooms only long enough to develop seed like ivory beads, this pretty shrub unnoticed and with no slightest hint of fragrance by day, waits until night has dropped her mantle and at that signal pours forth her

137

heart in full libation of thrilling and all-pervasive perfume.

Does the Chilli Pepper (*Capsicum minimum*) laugh at the cold name for his hot heart and glow with satisfaction at the necessity for his presence as a condiment at every Hawaiian *luau*, knowing that not even the marketed Bell-pepper (*Capsicum grossum*) flavorable but not hot, can supplant him?

ROSE FAMILY

LOQUAT

Photinia (Eriobotrya) japonica

The Loquat, familiar in our childhood, is rarely seen but is recommended for more cultivation as it is easily propagated by seed, or, better, by budding or grafting. It is a slender tree and is attractively planted in clumps. Its long and pointed velvet-backed leaves, heavily veined, and clusters of downy-skinned yellow fruit offer artistic arrangement in the house. When their beauty on the table has passed, the fruit is welcomed by the jelly-pot. The handsome large seed seems to be looking for appreciative lei makers.

SANDALWOOD FAMILY

HAWAIIAN SANDALWOOD —— Iliahi

Santalum freycinetianum

Tales that are told gather the fragrance of romance. So the closed chapter of the Hawaiian sandalwood trade with China which sped on golden wings, golden wood for golden metal, has left only the fragrance of a rare possession gone, if not forever, until centuries repair by the slow growth of this valuable tree the ruthlessly sacrificed forests. To think that once our Islands were called Tan-shan, "Sandalwood mountains," by the Chinese and that now the Laau ala (fragrant wood) is sought almost in vain! This is because although sandalwood is found on the different islands, in as many variations, it takes two centuries to ripen the real perfume. Visitors at the volcano walk the trail abutting on the crater of Kilauea and find young trees growing, but there is little glamour about them. Timber worth export was exhausted almost a hundred years ago. It behooves our youth to coax back the tree to its long-lived estate, splendid in height of lusty trunks. Mr. Bryan quotes from Dibble the historian a tale of Kamehameha's rebuke to those cutting young wood, declaring that it belonged to future generations. Let Hawaii become again a land of its sweet savor.

SOAP-BERRY FAMILY

This family is rather slightly represented in the Islands, by the Soap-berry, the Lichee, and one species of *Longan*.

SOAP-BERRY TREE —— A'e or Manele

Sapindus saponaria

The Soap-berry is one of our indigenous trees and in its native forests thrusts its buttressed columnar trunk up to eighty feet of splendid growth, but in the city the tree is small. Its bark is deciduous. It has oval leaves with entire margins, small yellowish flowers and hard round dark seeds which wear a little thin coat. These berries are used in Ceylon for rosaries and in Honolulu for leis.

LICHEE

Litchi chinensis

The name of this tree speaks its native land. The ancestor of the all too few Lichees in Honolulu still stands *waikiki* of Nuuanu Avenue just *mauka* of School Street. It was brought in 1870 as a prize for his own garden by Mr. A. Afong, one of the pioneer merchants from China who built themselves into the now homogeneous community of many races.

For many years the Lichee nut has been familiar through its importation from China for enjoyment at the Chinese New Year celebrations. A raisin-like thin pulp clings to the shiny dark seed after the skin of the fruit has dried to a fragile, corruscated brown shell.

This differs greatly from the fresh fruit which hangs in clusters the color and size of giant strawberries and from May to July makes ruddy the dome of the graceful tree in full foliage of pointed leaflets,—a surprise after the minute green flowers and a delight first to the eye and then to the palate. The shell to be is now a heavy leather well-tooled by nature and holds a juicy flesh rivalling that of a Muscat Grape. Being rare, the crop of a tree is always marketable at a high price.

Sometimes trees are sterile, but those that bear produce prolifically. The tree is, if planted from seed, slow of growth and maturity but is readily propagated from layers, and Honolulu should see to it that this admirable tree is increasingly planted.

TARO FAMILY

Taro or Kalo

Colocasia antiquorum, var. esculenta

By its flower the Taro declares itself kin of the
Calla Lily, Caladiums and other ornamental plants

APE PLANTS

familiar elsewhere. But not for ornament is the Taro
planted. As seed to the sower and as bread to the eater
of colder climates so is Taro to the tropic islander.
As fair as fields of wheat ripe unto harvest are the
flooded terraces ready for planting wherein the moon
mirrors her face; or the young crop of Taro with rain-
drops running like mercury over the surfaces of the
leaves; or the matured fields lying like Madame Na-

ture's pieced-quilt as one looks down from a high hill upon the bed of a cultivated valley.

The neutral taste of the cooked root is as satisfactory to the palate as the taste of potato, rice, or hominy, each to its habitual eater. When grown, it offers an easily digested and nourishing food, and while growing, gives the producer, after his work of planting is done, a year of leisure in which to meditate as he rests upon its banks.

Taro has several varieties and so has the allied Ape, a handsome plant but edible only under compulsion of food scarcity. The Ape has a leaf large enough to umbrella four or five children in a sudden shower. Its long, pointed flower, strident in odor, is most distinguished in character. Much as Sargent's Hosea (in his group of the Prophets) clutches his cloak under his chin, does the Ape flower hold its spathe tightly about its dawn-colored throat and its immaculate spadix.

Philodendron

The Philodendron, a genus of creepers from tropical America is known to have in its native countries one hundred and sixty-seven species. Several of them are well established residents of Honolulu.

From the name, "tree-loving" the plant is easily recognized, for it is a stalwart tree-climber, clinging to its chosen mate in life and often entirely obliterating the form of a defunct Palm or Algaroba with its heavy vegetation.

It is propagated by planting divisions of the climbing stem, the little foot-like roots that cling to the tree trunk adapting themselves well to draw nourishment from the ground.

The leaves of many varieties are large, sometimes elephant-eared; some are deeply cleft like Breadfruit leaves; others are perforated with great holes; one handsome variety is palmately lobed and a glossy dark green.

The Philodendron is monoecious, the flowers being borne on spadices somewhat resembling those of the Calla Lily, Ape, Kalo and other members of the Caladium family, to which they are kin.

The *Monstera Deliciosa* bears an edible fruit. Its spathe, when dry, makes a little flower basket as of thinnest brown wood.

A yard where many trees are consorted with these exuberant vines suggests a tropical jungle of dense and rich gloom.

TERMINALIA FAMILY

Kamani Haole

Terminalis catappa

This, the Kamani *malihini,* is often thought of as the Umbrella Tree and in some parts of the world is known as Indian Almond. Planted in some of the older gardens of Honolulu, it is a landmark on a part of the round-the-island drive where it makes self-planted thickets. It is truly deciduous and before its fall, which is a season somewhat uncertain in date, it is a blaze of autumn colors, its leaves, tapering from a broad curve at the top to end in a half inch petiole, suggesting gay fans as they flutter from the umbrageous branches, set horizontally, to carpet the ground. The flower is white and inconspicuous (all the glory gone to leaves) and the fruit is a hairy nut like a huge almond covered with a bitter-sweet pulp and thin skin tinted like the leaves. The nut holds an edible kernel that few but children trouble to extract. This handsome tree may attain a height of seventy-five feet but its first impression is of wideness. It would undoubtedly be more planted if gardens had room needed for its spread.

Quisqualis Vine

Quisqualis indica

This vine is one of those early introduced but rather rarely seen now. A large specimen clings to a house on Vineyard Street *waikiki* of Nuuanu Street. A very heavy one for many years adorned the old Royal Hawaiian Hotel, where the Army and Navy Y.M.C.A. building now stands. The abundant leaves are oval with entire margins. The flowers, five-petaled, with velvety texture and color shading from light pink to dark red, hang by long stems in full clusters. In India the vine is called Rangoon Creeper.

VERBENA FAMILY

Bleeding Heart

Clerodendron thomsonae

Commonly called by a sentimental name that has been given to many different plants, this Verbena, half-vine, half-shrub, cherishes its small scarlet corolla with a cream-colored calyx that deservedly scores as a part of the flower. Purplish stems, and purple faded bloom, together with pretty, dark green leaves, well set off the clusters of flowers with their winsome appeal.

Pagoda Flower

Clerodendron squamatum

This handsome garden shrub bears pagoda-shaped panicles of scarlet flowers which rise above the dark heart-shaped leaves. The flowers are succeeded by seed-fruits of midnight blue strikingly borne on vivid scarlet stems.

Sandpaper Vine

Petraea volubilis

This engaging climber, although it has rough-sur-faced leaves, deserves a better nickname than "sand-paper." It is sometimes mistaken for Wistaria by the newcomer, but the resident knows to his sorrow that Wistaria does not bloom in Honolulu. The Petraea flowers several times a year, its dainty starry flowerets arranged in long racemes, making a lovely mass of blue. It is particularly enjoyable if, having climbed the right tree, it mingles its sky color with the rosy clouds of the Pink Shower trees.

Golden Dewdrop

Duranta repens (or *plumieri*)

The Duranta was known in our grandmothers' gardens sixty years ago, but is even more valued today for a banking of graceful shrubbery. It grows to a height of from six to ten feet, has a full foliage of small and smooth green leaves and, whether giving white or lavender-blue panicles of dainty flowerets, follows the bloom with berry-like fruit (for birds only) of so deep a yellow as to give the plant its descriptive name. It is a native of tropical America.

145

Teak Tree

Tectona grandis

Another member of this family that is by most of us associated with sweet-scented garden flowers, is as rare as the Lantana is common. The tree is mentioned here because its name, Teak, is on the lips of all who haunt our Oriental furniture shops. Common belief has it that all the dark furniture of Chinese origin is made of Teak wood. Not only is this untrue, but it should be known that the hard and exceedingly durable Teak is, in the sapwood, white, and in the heart wood, a golden yellow which turns brown and mottled when seasoned.

Oi

Verbena bonariensis

This wayside bushy weed with single blue flowers strung scantily on an upright stem was an early comer. Though interesting, it is considered a nuisance.

Lantana

Lantana camara

Hawaii offers two paramount examples of the influence of environment in changing natural characteristics, the Mongoose in the animal kingdom and the Lantana in the vegetable. These illustrations call for pause in too swiftly decided importation. The Lantana, brought long ago as a pot plant, entered this land as the Israelites entered Canaan, to possess it. But, although long regarded as a curse because with thorny stride and barrier arms it made miles of territory its own, now that it has been vastly diminished by a parasite

146

imported to wage war upon the invader, it is found to have been a not unmixed evil. It has broken up poor soil, and, purged by fire, has laid down its life in splendid potash deposit. With less of it by the wayside, we behold its beauty of variegated color and its perfume, not too heavy in wind-swept spaces, and even suggest that the white variety which does not ripen seed (and so is not in cahoot with the Mynah bird for ubiquitous usurpation) might well be cultivated in gardens.

> Hands that are bruised
> May sometime render
> Thanks for what has made them tender.

INDEX

A

Acacia dealbata, 15
    decurrens, 15
    farnesiana, 12
    koa, 12
Acalypha hispida, 54
Acanthus family, 1
Adenathera pavonina, 30
A'e, 139
African Tulip Tree, 34
Agapanthus umbellatus, 78
Agathis australis, 125
Ainahau, 94, 95
Alakea Street, 20
Albizzia lebbek, 19
Aleurites moluccana, 48
Algaroba, 9, 10, 21
Allamanda carthartica, 130
    hendersonii, 129
Alligator Pear, 73, 74
Alpinia nutans, 59
    samoensis, 60
Althaea rosea, 70
Alyxia olivaeformis, 134
Andropogon schaenanthus, 62
Antignon leptopus, 38
Ape, 56, 141, 142
Aralia, 2
Aralia Family, 2
Araucarias, 126
Aristolochia elegans, 55
Artocarpus incisa, 89, 90, 91
Australian Cedar, 79
Avocado, 73, 74
Awapuhi, 57

B

Bachelot (Father), 9
Bamboo, 3
    Family, 3
    Grass, 61
    vulgaris, 3
Banana, 4, 56
    Family, 4
Banyan, 92, 93, 94
Barleria strigosa, 2
Bates Street, 18, 113
Bauhinias, 19, 20
Bean Family, 9
Beaumontia grandiflora, 131
Beretania Street, 37, 73
Bermuda Grass, 62
Be-Still Tree, 133
Bignonia Family, 31
    jasminoides, 32
    regina, 33
    tweediana, 32
    unguis-cati, 32
    venusta, 31
Bird of Paradise, 8
Bleeding Heart, 144
Bombax ceiba, 45
    ellipticum, 45
Bougainvilliea (brick-red), 36
    (brighter-red), 36
    Family, 35
    (magenta), 37
    (pink), 36
    (purple), 36
    (rose red), 36
    (white), 36

149

151

153

COLOR INDEX

157

PURPLE—*Continued*
  FRUIT—*Continued*
    Water Lemon (vine), 120
    Wine Palm (tree), 116

RED
  FLOWER
    Acalypha (shrub), 54
    African Tulip (tree), 34
    Aralia (tree), 2
    Awapuhi (plant), 57
    Bleeding Heart (bracts of
      white) (vine), 144
    Bougainvillea
      (varieties) (vine), 36
    Coral Tree, 29
    Crown of Thorns
      (shrub), 54
    Giant Ginger (large
      plant), 60
    Ginger (bushy plant) 60
    Hau (Mahogany color)
      (tree), 70
    Hibiscus (varieties)
      (shrub), 66
    Ie ie (vine), 117
    Ixora (shrub), 44
    Kuhio Vine, 87
    Lobster Claw (plant), 7
    Milo (Mahogany color)
      (tree), 73
    Ohia ai (tree), 99
    Ohia Lehua (tree), 98
    Oleander (shrub), 132
    Pagoda Flower (shrub),
      145
    Poinciana regia (tree), 21
    Poinsettia (shrub), 53
    Prickly Pear (tree), 39
    Pride of Barbadoes
      (tree), 28
    Roselle (shrub), 68
  FRUIT
    Avocado Pear (tree), 73
    Banana (tree), 4
    Banyan (tree), 92

RED—*Continued*
  FRUIT—*Continued*
    Carissa (tree), 130
    Castor Oil (tree), 54
    Christmas Berry (tree),
      84
    Coffee (tree), 43
    Lichee (tree), 140
    Night-blooming   Cereus
      (vine), 40
    Ohia ai (tree), 99
    Pomegranate (tree), 104
    Prickly Pear (tree), 39
    Strawberry Guava
      (tree), 104
    Tomato (plant), 135
    Wiliwili (false), 30
  BRACT
    Banana, 4
  LEAF
    Coleus, 52
    Kamani Haole
      (red variations)
      (tree), 143
    Young leaves of several
      t r e e s, conspicuously
      Mango.

VARIEGATED
  FLOWER
    Canna (plant), 78
    Gladiolus (plant), 78
    Hollyhock (plant), 70
    Lantana (shrub), 146
    Quisqualis (vine), 144
  FRUIT
    Chilli Pepper (plant),
      138
    French Cherry (tree),
      101
    Inga (tree), 16
    Kamani Haole (tree),
      143
    Mango (tree), 80
    Mulberry (tree), 87
    Royal Palm (tree), 113

160